SIR EDWARD APPLETON

Frontispiece: Sir Edward Victor Appleton (*by courtesy of* Stephens Orr, Glasgow).

SIR EDWARD
APPLETON

G.B.E., K.C.B., F.R.S.

by

RONALD CLARK

PERGAMON PRESS

OXFORD · NEW YORK · TORONTO

SYDNEY · BRAUNSCHWEIG

Pergamon Press Ltd., Headington Hill Hall, Oxford
Pergamon Press Inc., Maxwell House, Fairview Park, Elmsford, New York 10523
Pergamon of Canada Ltd., 207 Queen's Quay West, Toronto 1
Pergamon Press (Aust.) Pty. Ltd., 19a Boundary Street,
Rushcutters Bay, N.S.W. 2011, Australia
Vieweg & Sohn GmbH, Burgplatz 1, Braunschweig

First edition 1971
Library of Congress Catalog Card No. 74–133009

Printed in Hungary

08 016093 X

CONTENTS

LIST OF PLATES

List of Plates

11. Cavendish research staff (*courtesy of* Hills & Saunders)
12. Resignation from the DSIR
13. With younger daughter (*courtesy of* Associated Press)
14A. Receiving the Freedom of Bradford (*courtesy of* Yorkshire Observer)
14B. Receiving the Nobel Prize for Physics (*courtesy of* AB Reportagebild)
15. Presidential Address, British Association
16. Working on the Reith Lectures (*courtesy of* The Scotsman)

Between pages 162 and 163

17. State Visit of King Olav V to Edinburgh (*courtesy of* Associated Newspapers)
18A. Opening the Mullard Radio Astronomy Laboratory (*courtesy of* A. C. K. Ware (Photographers) Ltd.)
18B. With Lord Adrian and Lord Blackett (*courtesy of* A. C. K. Ware (Photographers) Ltd.)
19. At the URSI Commission on the Ionosphere
20A. The Cowan House Race (*courtesy of* The Scotsman)
20B. With Pandit Nehru (*courtesy of* George Outram & Co.)

Between pages 194 and 195

21A. With H.R.H. Prince Philip (*courtesy of* The Scotsman)
21B. Opening the Cameron House Youth Centre (*courtesy of* The Scotsman)
22A. An after-dinner speech (*courtesy of* Photo Illustrations (Scotland))
22B. At the tenth URSI General Assembly
23A. At a special graduation ceremony, Edinburgh (*courtesy of* E. R. Yerbury & Son)
23B. At C. T. R. Wilson's ninetieth birthday luncheon (*courtesy of* George Outram & Co.)
24A. With Mrs. Helen Allison, later Lady Appleton (*courtesy of* Beaverbrook Newspapers)
24B. Abden House, Edinburgh

viii

FOREWORD

THE legendary figures in the history of science are nearly all associated
in memory with specialised topics however full their lives may have been
of other events. In the last century of the physical sciences the names of
Maxwell, J. J. Thomson, Rutherford, or Einstein, for example, are
synonymous with electromagnetic radiation, the electron, the atom, and
relativity, but their lives were full of other important activities both
within and outside their particular science. Will the name of Appleton
similarly live in memory only as synonymous with the ionosphere?

He, himself, might well wish it to be so. It is the single coherent
thread throughout his life. However great his burdens elsewhere he continued his researches to the end. Forty years after his great discoveries,
at a time when he must often have felt overwhelmed with the problems
of Edinburgh, he was still making significant contributions to a subject
which like all other topics in science had grown enormously complex.
That is a measure of his devotion to science and of his continued mastery
of a subject which he had prised open as a young man.

In an earlier age Appleton might well have remained altogether in
his scientific laboratory. In fact, his life spanned the transitional stage
where science grew in stature to become a vital and expensive activity
of the modern state. Because of this he became a pioneer, not merely
in scientific research, but of the scientist who was called upon to play an
essential part in the administration of science. This he did with such

Foreword

distinction as Secretary of the Department of Scientific and Industrial Research during the years of the Second World War, and subsequently over a wider sphere as Principal and Vice-chancellor of the University of Edinburgh, that one cannot be certain now that in the context of history Appleton's name will inevitably and only be associated with the ionosphere. It is very hard indeed to find a parallel in the modern world of a scientist of such eminence who may well be remembered for his reign in two other distinct activities.

Appleton's science and his administrative duties were so inextricably entangled with the origins and development of radar that the future historian may well wonder why he was not also regarded as its father-figure and founder. I suspect that far more will some day be written on this subject and that Mr. Clark's avoidance of too deep a penetration into the affair has been conditioned by the necessities of the law of libel. Appleton was too great a man to descend to a public squabble, although indeed it is hard to believe that he was not greatly provoked by Watson-Watt's *Three Steps to Victory*, and even more so by Watson-Watt's address on "The Evolution of Radiolocation" at the Radiolocation Convention of the Institution of Electrical Engineers in March 1946 when he said:

> ...I would admit as founder members of the Radiolocation Club, A. P. Rowe, H. E. Wimperis, Henry Tizard, Philip Cunliffe-Lister, A. V. Hill, P. M. S. Blackett, Robert Watson Watt, A. F. Wilkins, E. G. Bowen, Adolf Hitler, and Hermann Goering. I would, in the most friendly manner, deny admission to Heinrich Hertz, to E. V. Appleton, to Briet and Tuve, and even to T. L. Eckersley...

Appleton had made his classic ionospheric investigations years before I was even a student, and when I first remember meeting him in the early years of the war the major scientific part of his career was over. Then, as Secretary of the DSIR, he was leading a delegation to the war-time establishment in which I was working. The new radar device which I was to demonstrate failed to work, but Appleton did not continue his tour until he had found out exactly what I had hoped to demonstrate,

Foreword

and left me with words of encouragement. Mr. Clark has related how, in later years and in an entirely different setting, Appleton was once again to help and encourage me. This attitude was typical of the deep interest which he displayed in the work of young scientists especially when their researches were related in any way to his own subject of radio science.

Appleton had a major impact on the development of science in the first half of the twentieth century, first by his own discoveries and later by his influence which extended throughout the international community of scientists. Mr. Clark's book is a record of a long and brilliant life. His account of Appleton's activities in so many diverse fields does ustice to the past and will be an inspiration for the future.

BERNARD LOVELL

AUTHOR'S ACKNOWLEDGEMENTS

MY MAIN thanks are to Lady Appleton who commissioned this life of Sir Edward, who gave me access to his papers in her possession, and who subsequently read the manuscript. Other members of his family to whom I am most grateful are his sister, Miss Dorothy Appleton, and his two daughters, Mrs. Lamont and Mrs. Appleton Collins.

Many members of the staff of Edinburgh University have been extremely helpful and I am particularly indebted to the Principal and Vice-Chancellor, Professor Michael Swann, and the Secretary of the University, Mr. Charles Stewart, for granting me access to Sir Edward's papers still in University hands, and to Professor W. E. J. Farvis.

My thanks are also due to Mr. J. A. Ratcliffe, for much advice and for reading the proofs, and to Sir Bernard Lovell for much advice and for writing the Foreword.

A very large number of those who knew Sir Edward have contributed both material and reminiscences, and I am particularly grateful to the following: Professor E. N. da C. Andrade; Professor W. J. G. Beynon; Sir Harold Bishop; Sir Lawrence Bragg; Sir Frederick Brundrett; Dr. K. G. Budden; Dr. Helmer Dahl; Hr. Olaf Devik; W. R. Darwin; Professor K. G. Emeleus; J. S. Hey; G. R. D. Hogg; C. Jolliffe; Professor R. V. Jones; Douglas Johnson; A. K. Longair; Professor A. J. Lyon; the late Sir Thomas Merton; G. Millington; Sir Philip Morris; Robert Naismith; W. R. Piggott; Dr. J. A. Saxton; Dr. R. L. Smith-Rose; Lt.-Col. F. T. Stear; A. F. Wilkins.

I also wish to thank Professor J. P. M. Tizard for permission to quote from Sir Henry Tizard's papers.

CHAPTER 1

1892–1919: THE ROAD TO THE CAVENDISH

A FEW years after the end of the war a group of graduates from Edinburgh University, all of them men from the West Riding of Yorkshire, met in Bradford for their annual dinner. Their chief guest was Sir Edward Appleton, Principal of the University, a Bradford man himself, Nobel prize-winner, and the distinguished scientist who had first mapped the ionosphere, that invisible outer shell of the earth's atmosphere whose existence makes long-range radio reception possible.

After the speeches, Appleton was approached by an elderly man who introduced himself as his former family doctor, a practitioner whose long experience encouraged him to ask a simple question. "How is it," he asked, "that a man of your great scientific distinction can emerge from an ordinary couple living in a back-to-back house in Bradford?"

Appleton replied, with a mixture of honesty and incomprehension, "I just do not know."

Question and answer are relevant not only to the mysteries of genetics which, with a casual inconsequence, can produce remarkable "sports" in plants, insects, and mice as well as in human beings, but also to the opportunities inherent in the bleak nineteenth-century working-class life which had so unexpectedly produced Appleton.

Bradford, it is true, has often enough produced its great men. Samuel Lister, whom Britain can thank for creating the Australian wool trade, was one of them. Delius the composer and Rothenstein the painter were others. Dyson the Astronomer-Royal came from Bradford, and so did the J. B. Priestley who modelled his immortal Jess Oakroyd on the father of a boy with whom Appleton went to school. Yet few of these men were born without some indication, on the family tree or in current circumstance, of fine things to come. Edward Victor Appleton was born without either, and his background, regarded dispassionately, has a quality much in line with Coulton's idea of the Middle Ages.

Even today, as one looks down into the straggling nest of streets which serpentinely crawl uphill and down dale to make Bradford, the prospect is grim. Three-quarters of a century ago it was more so, with Blake's dark satanic mills still occupying most of the valley floors. Above them there reached up and back not a green and pleasant land but the rough moors which rose westwards to the skeletal backbone of England. Little wonder that in the straight-built chapels there was such concentration on the life to come. Little wonder that pleasures had to be of the simple sort, and that the pattern for most lives was bounded by daily work, Sunday service, and the excursions of the Band of Hope.

It is a commonplace that all men wear, beneath the skin, the imprint of their childhood years, normally invisible but revealing itself unexpectedly in a multitude of small traits which can sometimes be identified. Superficially, the imprint on Appleton was less deep than on most men. When from middle life onwards he spoke as a distinguished guest at important functions, he spoke as one born to high places; at international conferences he appeared as a man who could speak as a peer among peers. Yet he still showed an innocent delight in success that was accentuated by the experiences of his early years, a lack of sophistication regarding the mechanics of power in high places, and an ingrained conservatism of outlook which at times tended to draw him towards the belief that authority must be right because it was authority. Despite his enjoyment of the best that life could give, the words proper, worthy, and moral inevitably push forward. It was one of Appleton's achievements that he could deserve such adjectives without appearing pompous; they were, in fact, part of the imprint stamped on him by his Bradford boyhood.

The Appletons are reputed to have come from Lancashire, although details are vague and it is recorded only that James, Appleton's paternal grandfather, was apprenticed to a chemist. He ran away from home, married, and founded a family of seven before dying in early middle age, as did his wife. Peter Appleton, Edward's father, was the youngest of the seven children, a trim, neat little man who married his wife, Mary Wilcock, on 24*s.* a week and who settled down in the late 1880's in a back-to-back in Bradford's Maperton Road.

The family was undeniably working class although Peter Appleton himself was not a mill worker. Instead, as his friends were later quick to point out, he was a warehouseman on the staff of Charles Semon & Co., Ltd., even though the warehouse was part of a mill. "He wore a bowler hat every day and I never remember having seen him in a cap," says one of young Appleton's contemporaries. "Most of the fathers nearby wore uniform, being railwaymen, policemen or postmen. In fact, it was a very respectable district in those days even though the houses were back-to-back." A choirmaster for 38 years in the local Wesleyan Chapel, Peter Appleton was also a member of the Alexandrian Quartette, well known at music festivals throughout the north, and a group whose prizes helped to augment his slender income.

Edward Victor was born on 6 September 1892 and christened after the tenor Edward Lloyd. He preferred his second name on the grounds that Edward was usually shortened to Ned or Ted, both of which he disliked. His birth was difficult, partly due to the broadness of his head, which was marked by the doctor's instrument, and family mythology maintains that one of the first people to see him was an old tradesman who called at the house selling muffins. "A fine head," is the legendary comment. "He'll go far, that lad."

When he began to attend Barkerend Elementary School at the age of 7, the young Appleton showed little more than persevering aptitude. However, three things held his interest. One was music. He enjoyed both the piano and the organ and was soon performing well on both. More remarkably, he taught himself not only to play but also how to read music. He also developed, at a later stage, a strong tenor voice, and more than once his father considered turning his son into a professional singer. The "tricks of the trade" which he learned from an early age — control of voice, ability to throw it just where he wished, elegance

3

of timing—were in fact to be of considerable use to him throughout life. But they were to help not on the concert stage but in the university lecture hall.

Appleton's second great interest was cricket. W. G. Grace was his hero, and while at school he not only decided, as many schoolboys will, that professional cricketing was the life for him, but at one time seriously considered it.

His third interest was the Band of Hope, whose pledge he had signed at an age when, as a contemporary says, "we were too young to write properly or understand what it was about". At the weekly meetings he took a prominent part in the singing, enjoying particularly the more robust hymns. There was also the annual outing on which the boys travelled in horse-drawn wagonettes, taking their own mugs for tea, and each carrying the long butterless currant bun with which they were issued before starting out. There were choir excursions into the Lake District and occasional long walks over the nearby moor, often led by Peter Appleton; and, when it could be afforded, there was the summer holiday for which Morecambe was usually picked.

This choice was largely dictated by the needs of Isabel, the thin frail sister who had been born to the Appletons 2 years after Edward Victor, a blue baby for whom in those days there was little hope. At Morecambe the girl could be pushed in her wheel-chair along the flat sands.

Until the age of 11 there was little remarkable about Appleton—except perhaps his appetite which is remembered across more than half a century. Appleton queueing up for the second bun; protesting "I could have eaten it" when a school-fellow turns away a second helping; regularly turning up at a friend's house every Thursday afternoon when the family baking would be followed by an extra-large tea; identified to his parents by a farmer's wife on a camping holiday with: "I can always tell which is your son—he's the one with the frying pan in his hand." These were, perhaps, the shadows cast by a man who was to praise moderation but was thoroughly to enjoy the good things of life.

He also kept pets—rabbits and cavies, white mice, white rats, and doves. He not merely kept them, but was held responsible for them. "I well remember," he said years later, "that this was laid squarely on my shoulders, and that if I went away on holiday, I myself had to arrange that someone else—a relative or a friend—would care for them in my absence."

At the age of 11, he won one of the rare scholarships to Bradford's Hanson Secondary School. When the results were announced, Appleton's name was top of the list—and the names were not, as was at first thought, listed in alphabetical order.

Appleton stayed at Hanson Secondary School for 6 years. An extraordinarily large number of people have remembered him—not only because of his later fame but also because, in the words of an old school report, "he displayed considerable force of character". The memories are not of those things which normally recommend a schoolboy to his fellows. Appleton was studious; he had a habit of coming out top; he appears to have had a stern worthiness which could easily have presented itself in extremely dislikeable terms. However, as in later life, he induced his companions to accept an earnest honesty. He was helped by being a good all-rounder in sport—and something of a "star" in cricket, football, and swimming—a stocky, well-built member of the athletics team who was well able to take care of himself.

It is typical that one colleague remembers Appleton for two things: that he was the only boy ever allowed to have a key to the physics laboratory—so that he could work in the evenings; and that he was captain of both football and cricket teams. Yet he was quiet; in the words of an old friend, "he never bothered to lose his temper with anyone"; and his good looks, trim appearance, and fine voice—all of which made him a favourite among the girls—combined to make up a picture rather different from that of the conventional "swot".

Thus he was popular—despite the thick, black 4*d.* note-book into which he jotted down details of interesting events and sayings, and his regular Saturday mornings in the Bradford reference library. "He was always talking about 'splitting the atom'," one of his school friends remembers, perhaps with a trace of hind-sight, "but then, I never understood what he meant." He read Dickens and Scott, encouraged by his grandmother Wilcock, but had a taste for lighter things as well, and for years his favourite reading was *Round the World in Eighty Days.*

But it was science, and particularly physics, which engrossed him. Just why he turned to physics is not clear — although an old school friend has suggested that he tended to look down on chemistry as being merely a test of memory. However, Appleton himself has suggested one link — "I was much influenced by my father's interest in music," he once wrote when asked why he chose to be a scientist. "And I suppose I was rather exceptional, as a boy, in studying Sir John Stainer's book on harmony and so on.... But I do remember, when I was 15 or 16, being much influenced by reading Gibson's *Introduction to the Calculus* and acquiring what I felt was a new power for dealing with physical problems of all kinds. After this experience I encountered Silvanus Thompson's *Calculus Made Easy* and, with the arrogance of youth, thought it very poor stuff indeed. However, I think it must have been largely the influence of my school Physics master, J. A. Verity, MSC, a Liverpool graduate, which made me specially fascinated with physics. By then the fame of the Cavendish Laboratory as a centre of modern physical research, under Sir J. J. Thomson, was even reaching the school, and I recall that, in my schoolboy mind, I was firmly determined to go to Cambridge. If I failed in this, King's College, London, was my second choice."

Appleton's ambitions suffered an early set-back. Although he won a Bradford City scholarship to the Bradford Grammar School at the age of 16 he did not take it up. The reason is not clear, but lack of money to keep him in the required station of grammar school life seems the most likely one. As it happened, rejection of the offer was to do him more good than harm, for he was now old enough to sit for the London Matriculation Examination where success would enable him to bypass further work at the grammar school. He sat, won a First, then prepared to take his Inter-BSC the following year. Technically he was still a student at Hanson, but the records of the Bradford Technical College — now the Bradford Institute of Technology — show an entry of: "E. V. Appleton — temporary Laboratory Assistant." How long he worked there is not known, but it is certain that his plans for going to London went on without interruption, and with a companion, Harry Halls, he booked and agreed to share lodgings in Fulham.

All therefore seemed to be set fair for London. Course was altered —

and Appleton sent on his way to the Cavendish at Cambridge—by a chance meeting in the streets of Bradford. Unexpectedly he came across his Science Master. And Mr. Verity, while being pleased at his student's success, demanded to know why Appleton was not sitting for the Isaac Holden Scholarship. Appleton replied, meekly no doubt, that he knew nothing about it. Verity enlightened him.

The scholarship, valued at £150 and tenable for 3 years, had been endowed in the memory of the late Sir Isaac Holden, a prominent Bradford citizen. Appleton sat for this without delay; won it; and then found himself, at the age of 18, financed for entrance to a Cambridge which would not admit him until the age of 19. This was perhaps as well, since he had to work up Latin and Greek, both compulsory entrance subjects which he appears to have tackled without undue difficulty.

The spare year was of significance in another way. Appleton had ample time for general reading and now came across Marr's *The Scientific Study of Scenery*. One result was that he decided to read geology in his first year as a tripos student, and mineralogy during his second. "As a result," he said, "I was awarded the University Wiltshire Prize in geology and mineralogy, a prize I didn't know about until I saw the announcement of the award in the *Yorkshire Post*."

The young man who prepared to leave Bradford for Cambridge still retained—as he was to retain throughout life—the imprint of his chapel upbringing. He had read the Bible from first page to last and was not ashamed of saying so. But as his eyes opened to the world around him, some at least of his early beliefs began to be shaken. Across 60 years a school friend remembers how Appleton had been gravely impressed by the Messina earthquake in which 77,000 men, women, and children had died, and how he expressed amazement that God could allow such things.

Much the same feelings no doubt filled him as he watched his mother coping year by year with the distressing problems of his young sister Isabel, a girl with a fine voice but no strength to use it, and whose life faded as she grew. Early in 1911 he wrote to a friend, a Miss Ada Leach, postponing a meeting.

"Isabel, my sister, who has been in bed now for ten weeks is growing rapidly worse; the doctor is coming every day and we are not leaving the house. My father and mother both think it would be best for me to stay at home for fear anything might happen. I am greatly disappointed for I have been looking forward so much to coming, having had a very poor Christmas owing to Isabel's illness." The sister died a few weeks later — some 2 years before the birth of Appleton's second sister, Dorothy, more than 20 years his junior.

Throughout the spring and early summer Appleton busied himself with preparations for Cambridge, and in the August began to kit himself out for his new life. His parents helped him by cashing an endowment policy, while his uncle Fred Wilcock presented him with five golden sovereigns. Early in September Appleton could inform Miss Leach that he was getting ready. "When I pack my belongings," he added, "your portrait will form one of them and in my room in college it will have a prominent position. If one of the tutors comes in and asks who you are I shall have to say, 'my cousin'."

Appleton went up to St. John's in the autumn of 1911, quite self-confident, suitably impressed with what he had already achieved, but also aware that he had reached a stairway on which he must move fast to remain in the same relative position.

One of the first things he did was to open an account with Barclay's Bank, addressing the envelope to Bene't Street rather than the usual "Benet" since, as he pointed out, the correct name was "Benedict". He was already conservative in outlook, and just as he continued to buy his stiff collars from the same Bradford shop for the whole of his life, so did he continue to keep his account at the branch at which he had opened it. Even when he moved to Scotland nearly 40 years later, he reacted in the same way to suggestions that he should close it: he had always been treated well there and really saw no reason for a change.

"College life was gracious living, even if it cost very little compared with today," he said half a century later of the Cambridge of 1911. "There was no published curriculum in any subject; and certainly our lecturers never attempted to cover a subject comprehensively. We students were expected to fill in the gaps by way of our own reading. It was thrilling to go to Sir J. J. Thomson's advanced lectures, for example, the subjects of which depended on the original papers he had just been reading at the time. This was my first experience of being brought to the frontier of knowledge by one who was himself engaged in advancing it."

His more personal reactions to a Cambridge which seems as remote from the present day as the Armada were given in a long series of cards and letters to Miss Leach, the first being a postcard showing the Dining Hall of Queens'. On this Appleton reported that he was getting settled in although lectures had not yet begun. "I have fine rooms of my own, and can feel my importance, I can assure you," he commented, before adding as a PS: "We at St. John's have a dining Hall even bigger and finer than this." His rooms were in New Court, duly marked with an X, and to these he returned for the Lent Term, writing in February that things were going well and that there was keen frost. "Fields which have been flooded have frozen and one can skate along for miles," he wrote. "I have been every afternoon this last week and have enjoyed myself thoroughly. Of course as there is so much room one can go twice or three times as fast as in Bradford and not be in danger of colliding with someone who is learning. I suppose the Parks in Bradford are frozen and that the ice is fairly good. I only wish the frost would last till Easter for my holidays, but I suppose there is no such luck."

His interest in hard exercise was increased when he began to appreciate how little time work normally gave him for it, and in the summer he played a lot of tennis, frequently squeezing in a couple of sets after lunch and cycling back to his rooms for a cold sponge and change before returning to the Cavendish. He also rowed, became a member of the Lady Margaret Boat Club, and prized his club blazer until the end of his life.

As in Bradford, he was an unusual mixture of sportsman and intellectual, as hard-going as most of his companions when it came to athletics but unwilling to lose more time than was absolutely necessary from the hard business of work. He was by this time also extremely good looking, with thick, wavy hair whose curls he found were unaffected by cream, water, or hard brushing. For the childhood memories of old ladies stopping to congratulate his mother, patting his cheeks, and then kissing him, were dreadful memories; the handsome head of hair in the mirror reminded him of them unduly.

Sir Edward Appleton

In June 1912 Appleton sat for the first part of the Natural Science Tripos, noting that "The papers have proved terribly stiff. I have had thirteen half-day exams so far and am waiting for four more. There will be nothing left of me soon, will there?" However, all was well. When the results were announced, Appleton was shown to have gained First Class Honours, the College Foundation Scholarship, and the Wiltshire Prize for special work in mineralogy. He returned to Cambridge during the Long Vacation to help in research which would continue during the next term. "My part of the investigation," he wrote, "is to find out how light travels through certain crystals — such tiny things about one-eighth of an inch square. Dr. Hutchinson advised two men who wanted to be taught mineralogy to come to me, so that now I have two pupils. It feels very funny teaching other people things, yet I like the work and as it swells my purse somewhat I do it."

The following term, Michaelmas, 1912, he decided to leave his college rooms and to move into lodgings, "partly to get away from too much social life", as he later remembered, but also, it seems likely, so that he could carry on with his mixture of learning and teaching. "I have been very lucky, for I have got a kind and considerate landlady," he wrote, "my rooms are very comfortable but one thing above all especially suits me — I have a piano.... I still attend lectures and have to sit under two famous men this term, Sir J. J. Thomson and Sir Joseph Larmor — both very gentle men who are always kind and considerate. The latter is so thoughtful that if he sees a new student he comes up to him and tries to make him feel at home. Also he seems to be able to make the most advanced things seem simple.... We still have the same invitations out to breakfast, tea, and coffee. I went to have breakfast with a man I know — a tutor of Clare College and he had some of the College silver plate on his breakfast table. Being a tutor, the College lend it to him now and then. Jove it was a gorgeous sight. Of course I suppose a girl would appreciate table things better than I. I have to go to the afternoon teas of our tutors' wives, and sometimes am bored to death. Then I begin to think that my place is among my books or in the laboratory. There I feel happier though of course now I have got somewhat used to these genteel functions."

The trappings that went with money fascinated him naturally enough, and when he was invited to dine with Sir Oliver Lodge the display of silver on the table was one of the things which impressed him. The other was Sir Oliver himself. "He said that he was the cleverest person he had ever met," Miss Leach remembers, "and that he was also the humblest; and he hoped that when he became a man he would grow like him."

It was presumably during this period that he also met Marconi for the first time, and Appleton later went on record as saying that he "soon came to understand one of the secrets of his [Marconi's] success. This was that he was never deterred from trying an experiment by a discouraging theory. He used to say, in conversation, that he *believed* that such and such a thing was possible—naming some result that existing knowledge suggested was unlikely or unattainable."

The following year Appleton was running up to Finals, studying 7 days a week but playing an hour's tennis every afternoon to prevent himself from getting stale. Already, confident in the results of the coming examination, he was planning what he would do next. "I have a lot of lines under consideration," he wrote. "If I do not see a good chance of staying on here as a tutor I shall probably go into the Civil Service (1st Division) or in the Indian Civil Service. Of course I can't say that my people would relish my going to India but it is here that money is made. Moreover, when a man is above forty-five he can come to England and retire on a pension of £1000 a year."

Once again his confidence was justified. This time he gained First Class Honours, the Hutchinson Research Studentship for mineralogy, and the Hocking Prize for distinction in physics. There was no difficulty now in his securing a temporary Cambridge post during the Long Vacation.

Working in the Cavendish in the summer of 1914 was Lawrence Bragg, just 24, the son of Sir William Bragg, Cavendish Professor of Physics at Leeds. Father and son were working together on X-ray analysis, for which they were to be awarded the Nobel Prize the following year. Part of the younger Bragg's work was done with his father in Leeds, part in the Cavendish. He required a collaborator, and it was Appleton who now joined him as his first research student. "I well remember," Appleton recalled long afterwards, "how he initiated me into the use of X-rays for

11

unravelling the architecture of crystals and how we worked out the structure of one or two metals together." And Bragg, reminiscing years later, comments: "I have often wondered whether, if it had not been for the war, he would not have become one of the leading X-ray crystallographers."

During their short time together they worked out the crystal structure of copper. But it was only in July 1914 that their joint work commenced. And on the day that Britain declared war, each man sought out the other in the Cavendish; each had the same thing to say—that the collaboration would now have to cease as each intended to join up.

Early in August 1914 Appleton applied for a commission through the Officers' Training Corps, of which he had been a member since coming up to Cambridge 3 years earlier. His first martial experience was as a member of the Corps, assisting his fellow officers to guard a reservoir on the outskirts of Cambridge.

"It was an all-night business, and of course we were told to look out for enemy agents who were likely to poison the water supply for Cambridge," he later remembered. "There we were, fixed bayonets and everything, posted at each corner of the reservoir. In the middle of the night I captured a little man who seemed to be snooping round the place. He tried to explain what he was doing, but, as this seemed to be my big moment, I wasn't in the mood for listening. But eventually, to my intense disappointment, I had to realise that I'd captured the night-watchman himself." However, he soon recovered from his disappointment—"I well remember how delicious breakfast tasted when I got back to College after being up all night."

After the first war-time flurries of excitement, Cambridge settled down to a period of waiting. By mid-September Appleton had tired of the process. He returned to Bradford and on the 20th enlisted as a private in the 16th Battalion, "The Bradford Pals", West Riding Regiment (the Duke of Wellington's).

The young man whom the recruiting sergeant accepted was 5 ft. $5\frac{1}{2}$ in. tall, with grey eyes and brown hair, and beside "Trade" on his Army book there went the words "University Coach". He was to serve in the ranks as private and then corporal, for 116 days, and while no record remains of his period of breaking-in, he seems to have coped with Army life without too much trouble. "I was prouder of the two stripes I then earned, before going to Aldershot for my RE training, than I was about any later military promotion I received," he later wrote.

This RE training began early in 1915. Appleton was luckier than many other specialists, for his qualifications were noted, his earlier application for a commission in the Royal Engineers eventually came through, and in a bleak January, he found himself at Aldershot, faced with the preliminary rounds of signal training and routine.

He wrote singularly little of his experiences during the First World War, either at the time or afterwards, but a few things stuck in his memory. One was his arrival at Aldershot. Almost half a century later, writing to an undergraduate who had joined the Army, he said: "I can sympathise with you about feeling a small undistinguished element on joining a great regiment. I felt exactly the same when I turned up, in 1914, in the Officers' Mess of Gibraltar Barracks, in Aldershot. However, I was made welcome by a much more senior officer and our friendship continued through and after the war— actually until his death some years ago."

In those days there was no Corps of Royal Electrical and Mechanical Engineers, let alone any Royal Corps of Signals, all communications work being handled by the Army Signal Service to which Appleton was now attached. This was to help decide the shape of things to come; for radio, first shown to be practicable by Marconi only a decade earlier, was just beginning to influence army communications, and the young Appleton was drawn into its development.

First, however, he had to be put through the mill. As an RE officer he had to ride. "I enjoy [it] fairly well," he confided to Miss Leach, "but the worst of it is that it is no ordinary riding. You see we are taught to ride without stirrups and without using the reins—in short we go through the regular course of Army drill. When you leave the Riding School you are 'some' rider I can tell you."

His life, a preparation for being sent to France in charge of a signalling section, began at 8 in the morning with cable laying and message sending, and continued until 7 at night with saddling horses, riding, inspection of stables, lectures on horses, visual signalling, lectures, and night

13

signalling. There were 70,000 troops in camp in and around Aldershot, as many as six aircraft could be seen in the air at the same time—apparently from nearby Farnborough—and there were occasional night manoeuvres. "Everything was arranged just as in real warfare for we had General Headquarters, Divisional HQ and Battalion HQ etc. with inter-communication," Appleton wrote of one to Miss Leach. "This was all done in the dark and in pouring rain. I was soaked, but on arriving home had a hot bath and about two hours sleep, for we had to be on parade again at 8 o'clock."

His training was completed in April, and but for his knowledge of radio he would now have crossed the Channel to France. Instead he was sent to Malvern where the first general radio course for officers was being given by Captain Trippe—the Trippe who later played an important role in industrial development of the thermionic valve. "Immediately Trippe had given us the first course and marked our examination papers, he fell so ill that he was unable to take on the next batch of officers for the second course," Appleton later said. "So I was sent for by the Colonel and told to carry on instructing the second course myself. Naturally I did carry on, but it was only later that I knew why the Colonel had dropped on me. Apparently I had come out first in the examination."

This chance illness of Captain Trippe was one of those incidents which, in retrospect, are seen to govern a man's life—just as, in Churchill's graphic illustration, whether a man walked to the left or to the right of a particular tree could make "the difference whether you rise to command an Army Corps or are sent home crippled or paralysed for life". For Appleton the difference was that he was not shipped to the battle front. Instead, he was posted to the RE Signals Depot at Fenny Stratford on whose staff he was to remain for the rest of the war.

Appleton's work was to be mainly technical. But at Fenny Stratford he learned more than one lesson for the future. "I had a commanding officer who spent most of his time in ensuring that no one of his junior officers ever made a mistake", he remembered 40 years on, when he was Principal and Vice-Chancellor of Edinburgh University. "We found his influence stifling. He was succeeded by a man who left us to our jobs, but jumped on us fiercely if we let him down. And it was precisely because he trusted us completely that we did our utmost *not* to let him down."

With the prospects that opened out as an instructor, Appleton decided to marry. But the bride was not to be Miss Leach, as one might have expected from the long letters signed "your sincere friend", but another acquaintance from his Bradford youth.

This, the daughter of the Rev. and Mrs. J. Longson, was Jessie Longson, a vivacious, dark-haired girl, a distant cousin of the Appletons who had been to school at Hanson but whom Appleton first met when she visited the family for a musical evening. She had a good soprano voice, and had been accompanied by him on the piano. The friendship had grown during the years. Miss Longson had gone to the Bradford College of Art on leaving school and had later become one of the first women textile designers in Bradford, working for Listers and creating designs to be woven in silk. She seems to have been talented beyond her opportunities, and in later life tended to regret the limitations which she felt had been forced on her. The fact that she could later push on her husband with a vigour that reinforced his own ambition did not entirely compensate for the situation.

The young couple married in 1916, and it is significant of the conditions in which Appleton had been brought up that the marriage raised a chorus of neighbourly "I-told-you-so's" around his parents' heads. They had been warned of the stupidity of sending the boy to a university; now, at the age of a mere 23, he had married; and now he would never pay back his parents for all the sacrifices they had made for him. That was the cry, and it was powerful, even though unjustified.

Soon after his posting to Fenny Stratford, Appleton brought his wife south to a cottage which he shared for a while with another lieutenant and his wife. Young married officers were comparatively rare, and in some ways Appleton appears to have been almost an odd man out. Certainly he took little part in the normal mess activities, and it was partly to evade bridge that he began to learn the conjuring tricks at which he became an accomplished amateur—producing half-crowns from behind children's ears with a casualness that never failed to delight them. He was also ambitious, a trait already apparent in his Cambridge vacation work, and when living in the mess would invariably search the papers first thing each morning to see whether he had been promoted — a habit which earned him the title of "Ack. doublepip".

His position as an instructor and a married man, coupled with the fact that he remained in England for all except a fortnight of the war, shielded him from much of the rough-and-tumble of Service life. Thus in later years colleagues who knew little of his early life would express surprise that a man who had served in the Army throughout the war should have retained his air of innocence, the impression that he was in some ways cocooned off from life. This was true in that he escaped much of the harsh realities of war. Yet in another way it was a useful attitude which he could assume or emphasise whenever he wished. He did so frequently, with great success, and fooled many people with it.

One quality which quickly became apparent was Appleton's ability as a lecturer. His was the task of describing radio to men who knew nothing of its theory and little of its practice. "His explanations," writes one who remembers him well from those days, "were so lucid and given in such an interesting manner that I found I had no difficulty in understanding the theory involved, and quickly learned the practical use of numerous pieces of apparatus. In fact I was so interested by those lectures that I decided to study electrical technology if I were lucky enough to survive the war."

This apparatus was of the most primitive kind. Thermionic valves were not in normal use, and a spark-sending set and a crystal detector was standard equipment. The set was called the British Field set and worked on 300–400 metre wavelengths. "It gave lots of trouble, which seemed in keeping with its description — the BF set," Appleton has said. "We also had more powerful sets for work in lines of communication, using Marconi rotary spark gaps and also Telefunken quenched-spark gaps. The former when running made a terrible noise like the sound of tearing calico and indeed if you were working over very short distances, as was the case during training, you could often read the signals better with the head-phones off, standing outside the lorry."

Early in the war Appleton played a minor part in unravelling one particular mystery — an early and classic example of the impact of science on battle. In 1915 the British forces in France found that they were suffering heavy casualties among ration parties taking supplies up to the forward areas. The Germans appeared to have accurate information on time and place, and however frequently these were changed, the ration parties found themselves under heavy artillery fire, which only started as they arrived on the scene and which ended immediately their job was done. About this time, but quite independently, the French discovered an enemy instrument which, after unsuccessful investigation, they handed over to the British. This found its way into the hands of what was later described as the "big three" of RE Signals. One was Captain, later General Fuller, who before the manufacture of thermionic valves invented the dynaphone, a device for amplifying wireless signals, and who was now an instructor with the RE Signal Service Training Centre at Woburn. The second was Captain Stevens and the third was Appleton. The three men eventually found the connection between the instrument and the shelling, and although Appleton has gone on record as saying, "I want to emphasise that it was from the brain of Major Fuller that the real solution emerged," all three were involved.

The German apparatus was found to be a two-valve amplifier with two pairs of phones and perhaps a dozen pairs of terminals with a switch either to each terminal or to each pair. The British Signals experts tried earthing the terminals; immediately they did so they found all the Army telephones in the area coming in loud and clear. The Germans had been sending out at night parties whose members planted earth pins among the barbed wire of the forward British positions and who then led wires back to their instrument. They were then able to pick up the signals from the earth return, switching out all except the one they wanted.

"Two solutions to this trouble were found, one obvious and the other not so obvious," Appleton later wrote. "The obvious one was to use double twisted wire. There was then no current flowing in the earth, since it was confined to a cable when travelling in both directions, out and back. Also the fact that the cable was twisted meant that there was no induction.

"However, double twisted cable was more expensive than a single wire, so an entirely different solution, still using an earth return, was evolved. It is true that Major Fuller, Captain Stevens and myself were involved in long discussion about these matters; but I want to emphasize that it was from the brain of Major Fuller that the real solution emerged. He invented what we called the Fullerphone, which replaced the vibrator as a signalling instrument. This cut down enormously the distance at which an earth return could be tapped."

The Fullerphone was first tried out experimentally at the end of 1915, and the following year was sent out to France in quantity, although owing to its delicate adjustment, operators needed special instruction. Its use became firmly established, and before the end of the war many divisions in France had adopted it for all forward circuits.

In the autumn of 1917 Appleton made a fortnight's instructional wireless tour in France, and during this showed both that the Fullerphone would work with as little as a micro-ampere of direct current, and that if a three-valve amplifier were used it could be utilised for listening to enemy signals. "In those days thermionic valves had bright filaments," he has written, "and I remember the incident of a senior RE officer coming into a dug-out and saying, when he saw such an instrument, 'Your electric light isn't very good here.'"

Appleton's spell in France lasted only until the end of December 1917. At first it had been planned that he should remain with 4th Army. However, a few days after Christmas, he wrote to his mother and father "The Colonel has told me today that they have telegraphed back from England to say I am not to be kept but am to return next week-end. So now I can throw my cap in the air and know for certain that I am not to be kept here. The main point is that I shall get leave when I get back and so shall come to see you all. Jessie will be excited when she knows the exact day.

"I hope you had a jolly Xmas day. Ours was very very quiet but we had Turkey and plum pudding. I believe they managed to give everybody in France that. Is it not wonderful?"

Thus Appleton returned from France. But he returned with, among other things, a German thermionic valve. This valve, together with the problem of measuring accurately just how strong radio signals really were, continued to intrigue him. The problems were, as he says, "put on the shelf" in his mind; when he returned to Cambridge early in 1919 they were to lead him further into his chosen field. "Further" since he had by this time already produced the first items in what was to be his vast output of papers, lectures and notes – an article in the *Wireless World* on "A thermionic valve slopemeter" and a "Note on the production of continuous electrical oscillations by the three-electrode valve" in *The Electrician*.

CHAPTER 2

1920–1924: POST-WAR CAMBRIDGE

IN THE spring of 1919 Appleton returned to Cambridge and was soon afterwards elected a Fellow of St. John's. When he had left the Cavendish 5 years previously he had only a general interest in physics, an interest that ranged across the whole subject and had been only momentarily pinned down to crystallography by the joint work with Bragg. Now he had a firm interest in radio, in the methods by which electromagnetic waves could be transmitted from one point on the earth's surface and received at another, a new and potent method by which one man could transmit ideas to another. And now he was married, a fact which added a further spur to his native wish to make good, to make his mark, to justify the courage of his parents in helping to send him to Cambridge.

For a year he worked as a research student in the Cavendish under J. J. Thomson, a frugal year which was probably harder than his previous year as an Army officer. Then, with Rutherford appointed Director, Appleton came on to the staff as an assistant demonstrator of physics, a confident step on to the first rung of the ladder.

Thus he was lucky. For he joined the most illustrious laboratory of its kind in Britain just as its new chief was to launch it on what later generations have considered its Golden Age. Only a few months earlier Rutherford had finally confirmed in Manchester that the atom was not a solid billiard ball of matter: that it was, instead, a complex mass of whirling particles: and that some of these particles could even be used to change one substance into another—apparently the transmutation of matter that had been the alchemist's dream down the centuries. Great possibilities were being opened out, largely by Rutherford's personal initiative. And to the Cavendish there was now drawn, by the attraction of genius, the small band of men who were to write the prologue to the nuclear age—Chadwick, who had been with Rutherford in Manchester, from a prison camp in Germany and later Cockcroft from the Army and Manchester; J. J. Thomson's son, fresh from aeronautical research. C. T. R. Wilson, whose cloud chamber was so elegantly to reveal the tracks of individual particles, had been there for many years, while J. J. himself still worked and held court in the laboratory. And coming up to the Cavendish under a special scheme for ex-naval officers was a group which included the young P. M. S. Blackett and, more unexpectedly, the younger, 20-year-old Sub.-Lt. Mountbatten, both of whom were to attend Appleton's lectures. Over all there ruled Rutherford himself, larger than life, directing, admonishing, encouraging, a massive intellect simmering away within the equally massive frame of a New Zealand farmer.

Into this exhilarating society Appleton plunged with a mixture of excitement and ambition. He worked at his allotted desk on the first floor of the Cavendish. He worked in his rooms at St. John's—in the First Court for two terms and then in a New Court set whose deep windows overlooked the Backs. At times he worked at home, in the top-floor study of the house he had leased in de Freville Avenue, a small, terraced house of such unprepossessing character that his wife had sat down and wept when she saw what was to be her first real home.

This three-way split in the background to Appleton's work meant that his view of the Cambridge society within which he now moved was less partial, and less enchanted, than that of a typical university don. He was intrigued but astounded by the built-in resistance to change which he noted, and was fond of quoting one don who in the 1920's boasted that he had never been inside a cinema. "He made the remark," Appleton would say, "in a way which showed he expected admiration all round, and the sad thing is that he got it—nearly all round." It is true that the sense of enduring traditions, the colourful flummery, the college plate and the historic figures who had looked down from the walls on eight or twelve or sixteen generations of Cambridge scholars all provided aspects of Cambridge life that now began to exercise a growing fascination over Appleton; but he was not blind to the other side of the coin. "My old Cambridge friend, T. R. Glover, used to tell me that there were three ways of being unpopular in Cambridge," he once said. "One was to be known outside Cambridge. Another was to know something about a subject other than that which you had taken in your degree examination. And the third was to be able to write simple English which anybody could understand."

In the 1920's conditions in some of the colleges still retained an almost medieval air. Appleton was fond of illustrating this by two stories in particular. "I remember," he would say, "when the Junior Bursar, a physiologist as it happened, suggested that baths should be built in the college. It was first pointed out in protest against the idea that term only lasted 3 months. Then there was one out-and-outer who said 'Over my dead body', or something like that. 'There have never been baths before'. And he then used the old rallying cry of mutual admiration: 'Surely you must admit the College is perfect as it is. It is so wonderful it could not be improved.' " Appleton would agree that baths were eventually built. "But," he would say, "I'm quite sure that some of the older ones felt they were hitting back for the rest of their lives by never using them or even looking at the building from outside."

There was also the affair of the cockroaches in St. John's kitchens. Appleton recommended that they should be dealt with. "But Mr. Brindly, the steward, opposed my recommendations most strongly," he later said. "Not because he was steward, but because he was a biologist. He pointed out that our particular species of cockroach was a rather rare one, having been brought over from the Continent some time during the reign of Queen Elizabeth, and he was very anxious that the particular strain should not die out."

Appleton tended to regard all this from an amused, exterior position. Yet at the same time it had its effect, making him "a Cambridge man" in every emotional nuance of the phrase and lodging in his mind at a comparatively early age the idea that the Mastership of St. John's and the Cavendish Chair were two of the pinnacles to which any man might aspire.

Like so many at the Cavendish, he was nearly steered into Rutherford's own field of nuclear physics, and at one time appears to have been deployed directly on Rutherford's nuclear work, trying to detect single alpha particles by the magnetic effect they produced when going through a coil. "But I wanted to work at radio," he wrote later. "After listening to my plans, Rutherford encouraged me to go off on my own—and I always had his warmest support afterwards." And it was through Rutherford that Appeleton first met Niels Bohr, the Danish genius as great as Rutherford himself and a man with whom Appleton was to develop a close and personal friendship.

Two things appear to have dissuaded Appleton from being drawn permanently into nuclear research. First there was his own experience on radio during the war; this had intrigued him, had suggested the potential waiting to be exploited, and had driven home to him how very little was known about either the creation of radio waves or the manner in which they were propagated through the atmosphere. This natural interest in radio would, alone, have been sufficient to deter him from concentrating on Rutherford's nuclear work. However, it seems likely that this natural inclination was reinforced by another reason. Rutherford was an established leader in the nuclear field; whoever followed him would, for years at least, be trailing at the end of a comet, a process never to Appleton's liking. Right from the start of his scientific career he appears to have been seeking for some field, some speciality, in which he would be able to gain, and hold, the position of unchallenged leader. So, to start with, he had radio.

This work, on which he embarked during his first post-war years at the Cavendish, fell under three headings. There was first, and possibly most important, his investigation of the way in which valves actually created radio waves—a direct result of his experiences in the war, during which he realised that although wireless valves were being used with increasing success, their operators had only a casual understanding of the ways in which they worked. Secondly, there was the problem of atmospherics, the frequent interruptions of radio reception about which little was yet known. Thirdly, he investigated the propagation of radio waves. Even in war-time, the variable nature of the received signals had been puzzling, and Appleton decided to discover why this was so.

In all of these investigations he was to be closely connected with the Radio Research Board, a government organisation set up in 1920 under the Department of Scientific and Industrial Research and charged with directing "any research of a fundamental nature that may be required, and any investigation having a civilian as well as a military interest". Rutherford was a founder member of the Board, whose main research station was sited at Ditton Park, Slough, on the site of the Admiralty Compass laboratory, and from its early days co-operation with the Cavendish was close. Appleton was receiving grants from the Board for his work almost from the day of his return to Cambridge and was an original member of its sub-committee on thermionic valves. And, as we shall see, the exploration of the ionosphere on which his fame rests was started with the support of the Board and then continued with its increasing help over the years.[1]

Appleton's first important investigations in post-war Cambridge were into the characteristics of the thermionic valve, invented only a few years previously by Fleming, and quickly becoming the most formidable weapon in the armoury of wireless. He had brought with him to Cambridge the German valve as well as a number given to him by British manufacturers, and for some while these were the only ones in the Cavendish. One fact about the valve which intrigued Appleton was its non-linear voltage-current characteristics; in other words, the relationship between these two quantities did not remain constant, and when one was plotted against the other the result was not a straight line but a curve.

He now set to work to discover what the effect of this non-linear characteristic would be when the valve was put in an electric circuit. With him there worked a young Dutchman, Balthazar Van der Pol, who had earlier been a research student with Appleton and who had then returned to Haarlem. Soon after Appleton started work as an assistant demonstrator, Van der Pol wrote to him suggesting that they might exchange ideas with

---

[1] Appleton became a member of the Board itself in 1926, served on it until 1939, and was also a member of the Committee on Propagation of Waves; the Committee on Atmospherics; the Committee on Thermionic Valves; and the Committee on Apparatus. He was chairman of the Ionospheric Wave Propagation Committee from 1946 to 1953, of the Ionosphere Committee from 1953 to 1957, and served on the Upper Atmosphere and Ionosphere Committee from 1958 until his death in 1965.

the aim of producing joint papers. Appleton enthusiastically welcomed the plan. "I am only too eager to fall in with it," he wrote. "I see in it a very happy way of consolidating our friendship. The first draft of my paper is nearly finished and I will send it to you to look over. Please don't send yours to me just yet as I am very busy indeed [in term]. Also my part seems to be more revolutionary, so I want you to criticise it carefully.... This is only a short note but I want to say how I appreciate your plan. My wife sees the sentimental side of the collaboration and is very happy about it." The significance of the joint work on which Appleton and Van der Pol now embarked has been well emphasised by J. A. Ratcliffe, future Director of the Radio Research Station: "The importance of what they did," he wrote in his Royal Society memoir of Appleton, "was that in the valve they had found a device which was markedly non-linear and whose non-linearity was controllable. By studying effects which it produced they learnt to understand more clearly the part played by much smaller and uncontrollable non-linear effects which were present in other cases."

This was early in 1920, and the friendship was to continue until Van der Pol's death more than 30 years later. There appears to have been no hard and fast division of labour, although Appleton seems to have carried out most of the experiments and to have leant upon Van der Pol for the intricate mathematical work involved. "It is only the first draft," he wrote typically on one occasion, "but I thought it advisable to send it on to you for *additions* and *corrections* on left-hand pages." Each man fertilised the other's mind, although their joint efforts produced only two papers—"On the form of free triode vibrations" and "On a type of oscillation-hysteresis in a simple triode generator", both published in the *Philosophical Magazine*.

Publication was, then as now, the mark of success, and Appleton's letters to Van der Pol show the continuing anxiety of a man fearing that competitors might get ahead of him. "I think it is essential to get it in quickly or someone else may be doing it," he writes on one occasion. On another he emphasises: "When this is finished we must hurry on with our article.... We must not delay or there will be somebody on it." And after he has seen a colleague's paper he writes: "I know that our names are on the first page. Thus a little more publicity."

The regular letters between Appleton and Van der Pol were supplemented by visits. The Dutchman came to England, and in the spring of 1921 and 1923 Appleton and Jessie visited the Van der Pols in Haarlem, taking with them their young daughter Margery, who had been born in 1920.

The Van der Pols had a son and two daughters – one of the latter christened "Ducky" as this was what Appleton always called her – and from the early 1920's the letters between the two men describing their wireless theories, on new pieces of equipment, mathematical problems, and the continuing mysteries of wireless, are increasingly interspersed with family news, with mutual regards for wives and children, and with comments on the exchange of presents.

The correspondence gives a good picture of Appleton's contemporary interests and of the society in which he moved as well as casting light on his own fears and foibles. He proudly writes: "Last night we had a feast in St. John's and I had as my guest C. T. R. Wilson." He notes that "after Xmas dinner, thought of simple way of developing measurement of signals idea." He had great plans for a book on the thermionic valve and told Van der Pol that the family was "going to the Isle of Man this Xmas so that I can give the whole of my Easter vacation (here and in Holland) to the writing of the book". And he was full of talk about Margery. "Baby can now talk very well and says all kinds of things," he told the Dutchman. "She often says 'So groot Dors' and 'Niet Dora', and 'Vow', and 'Ja, ja, ja'. The curious thing is that if she hears the word Dora or Ducky, she immediately says the other Dutch words. So great is the association."

Van der Pol was attracted to Cambridge in much the same way as Appleton, and early in 1922 he sounded out his friend on the chances of gaining an appointment in the University. Appleton's reply casts interesting light on his own position. "I have not yet had time to sound Rutherford about the question of your coming here, but I am going to put before you the facts as I find them," he said. "In the first place one could only make up to £700 or £800 a year with a Fellowship (£200). There is no lectureship higher than about £250 per year. And of course Fellowships are reserved for members of colleges as you know. At present there is a tremendous drop in prices and a wholesale cutting of wages and salaries. Jobs are hard to get and people who have them are sticking for all they are worth to them. Thus I feel that if you came and got, say, a lecturing post of £300 per year with only about five hours work per week the rest would have to be made by coaching which of course would destroy all the originality for research which you possess. Coaching is at the rate of £12 per term for three hours per week. There are three terms per year so that a lot of time must be given up to coaching to make an income of it.... When my Fellowship lapses as it will after six years is up I shall be reduced to about £650 a year, and if I wanted to do more research than I do now I should have to drop some teaching and get even less."

Thus the prospects at Cambridge were not particularly encouraging — either for Appleton or for Van der Pol who now accepted a post in the Eindhoven research department of Philips, the firm with which he was to work for the rest of his life. From this date technical co-operation between Appleton and his Dutch colleague decreased. This was partly, no doubt, due to the limitations which Van der Pol now felt about his commercial work — "Of course, I don't know how far you are allowed to discuss these things openly with me because of Philips..." Appleton wrote. Another factor was Van der Pol's publication of a paper to which Appleton took exception, against which he protested, and which drew from Van der Pol the pained reply that: "The paper was written in the spirit intentionally *not* to publish anything that was specifically yours *and which was not published yet in the scientific journals.* And I think I *completely* succeeded in that." A third factor may well have been Appleton's feeling that Van der Pol, working with the weight of the Philips organisation behind him, was already his equal and might soon draw ahead. Appleton did not abandon the particular field which he had begun to explore with the Dutchman, and his book *Thermionic Vacuum Tubes* was eventually published in January 1932. It ran through five editions before being completely revised and rewritten by W. H. Aldous and Appleton in 1952 — and was still bringing in royalties 30 years after the original edition had appeared.

However, from the mid-1920's, the emphasis of Appleton's work began to move elsewhere. He had, moreover, a good strong second string to his bow. This was the study of atmospherics, the electrical disturbances which originate in lightning flashes and can so seriously interrupt radio reception. His interest was strongly stimulated by his friendship with C. T. R. Wilson, also working in the Cavendish, and at this period carrying out his pioneer work on thunderstorms. Appleton tried to relate what Wilson was discovering about lightning flashes to what he already knew about wireless atmospherics, and for some while the two men worked virtually in collaboration, Appleton using Wilson's special aerial and hut off the Madingley Road, the hut with its aerial being the only elevated object over a fairly level stretch.

"I will now tell you a little of what I am doing," he wrote to Van der Pol soon after the start of this work. "I hope to get records of electric field changes during lightning flash by allowing field to deflect cathode ray beam itself (i.e. without plates) and in testing various other things I find that a valve can be used as a measurer of *actual radiation*. By using valve with open filament and anode and using emission velocities of electrons only and sensitive galvanometer one can detect an alternating field of 1/2 volt per cm. The field makes the electrons miss the anode and the current is reduced. Is there any use for this in measuring radiations near a large antenna?"

Another letter to Van der Pol—written on 10 June on the new typewriter which Appleton thought would prove useful for papers and the projected book—illustrates what was to become a recurrent problem in his life—the difficulty of finding adequate time for research when other duties pressed in on him. "I am now in the midst of examinations, and life will be terrible until the end of the month when you arrive in England," it goes. "Still I am keeping the spark of research alive and have succeeded in doing what I suggested some time ago. In conjunction with Mr. Gibson, a Wireless Research Student, I have measured the C.W. signals from North Weald Station (70 kilometres away) directly by measuring the 'silent space'. Captain Round of the Marconi Company has very kindly given me all particulars of the station and is going to send me special signals in a few days. The method works beautifully for strong signals. We find on an aerial of a few metres effective height that the total E.M.F. introduced in the system is from 26/10 000 to 36/10 000 of a volt. We can easily tell when they alter their antenna current by a few per cent. So the measurement of E.M.F.'s of a few thousandths of a volt can be done with accuracy."

His aim was to discover the relationship between thunderstorms and atmospherics, and his letters to Van der Pol constantly refer to his progress. "I have something a bit more important," he wrote on 23 May 1922 after describing his valve work, "and that is that my electric wave detector has detected the electric field discharge beautifully in thunderstorms six or eight miles away — a direct indication of the earth's field."

This work on atmospherics quickly brought Appleton into contact with a man whose course was to cross and counter-cross his own for the rest of their lives — R. A. Watson-Watt, an ambitious young Scots physicist of Appleton's own age. In 1920 Watson-Watt was also trying, at a meteorological out-station in Aldershot, to decipher the connections between thunderstorms and atmospherics. The following year this work was brought under control of the Radio Research Board, and shortly afterwards Appleton and Watson-Watt were working together, sometimes in Cambridge, but more frequently at Aldershot. They were soon using a cathode ray oscillograph — an instrument in which quickly-varying electrical quantities are not only recorded visually but are recorded permanently on film — to record the waveform of individual thunderstorms, the storm's individual finger-prints, as it were. Appleton discovered, as he wrote to Van der Pol, that "atmospherics are found to be of two different classes, (1) long aperiodic ones, and (2) short periodic impulses with fairly strong damping. The latter give a sharp click in the telephone while the former give more of a growl."

Much of this work was primarily for Service use. "It is beautiful doing things for the Army and Navy as it takes no time," Appleton commented. "You just draw out the circuit and make suggestions and they do all the experimental labour. There is also plenty of *money*, and no difficulties about apparatus. I have only to go to the place twice to see that all was as I wanted." He became increasingly drawn into the work, and in the summer of 1924 could write: "Thunderstorms have given me no rest the last three weeks. I have got 700 readings on flashes, and now can have a rest and get back to writing. I had to take the chances as one cannot produce flashes to order."

The "give me no rest" was typical of Appleton throughout the whole of his life, but rarely more so than now. He was 32, a man remarkable for his energy, his variety of interests, and the way in which he could find time for further work or for necessary exercise. It was typical that as less time could be found for tennis, or for the golf which he had recently taken up, these pastimes should be replaced by something that could be fitted more easily into life — exercise on an improvised punch-ball on the little landing at the top of the stairs in de Freville Avenue.

Appleton's work for the Services with Watson-Watt during this period, and his comment on how beautiful it was to co-operate with them, raises an interesting possibility.

It was during this period that the Navy, the Air Force, and to a very much lesser extent the Army, were slightly if sluggishly altering their attitude to science. The Admiralty created a Directorship of Scientific Research, and the Air Ministry followed suit — in both cases appointing at the top men with whom Appleton was to be closely connected. He himself must have been looked upon with speculative eye, particularly as Rutherford was constantly consulted by the Services in such matters, as he was about almost everything impinging on science. But Rutherford's natural interest in keeping a good man in his own laboratory no doubt helped to squash any suggestion that Appleton might have been co-opted into permanent government work. So did his own natural inclinations. As always, his prime interest was in academic research, for its own sake, regardless of possible applications. In later life, particularly after his experience at the DSIR during the Second World War, he would stress that the barrier between pure and applied science was at times a vague one, that the two were inseparably linked, and that if man was to make the most of his possibilities in the world, then both must be utilised like the twin horses drawing a chariot. Yet there could be no doubt that for Appleton pure science provided the main attraction.

His interests did flow over into other channels, but partly on account of the need for cash. Like many other married university men, he found it necessary to take on much extra work to make both ends meet. "My mother told me," says his elder daughter, "that he never paid tradesmen's bills until the men called for the money, and she was horrified the first time the coal merchant arrived for his money, but he comforted her, saying that 'all the gentlemen were the same' – so it must have been the fashion in those days to keep tradesmen waiting." For Appleton it was not only the fashion but frequently a necessity. Therefore he coached as much as he was able, conscientiously but not liking it over-much. And therefore he began to take up the first of various industrial consultancies and advisory appointments, a practice less usual then than now, and one which raised Cambridge eyebrows among the few academics to whom the facts leaked out.

What appears to have been the first of such appointments came after Appleton had demonstrated a Mullard R-type valve to a group of men to whom he was acting as supervisor between 1920 and 1922. He concluded by explaining that the valve was, surprisingly, capable of receiving a signal from New York. As his undergraduates were leaving he turned to one of them, H. J. Pye, whose family ran the Cambridge electrical firm. "Pye, is your firm doing anything in connection with this new wireless boom?" he asked. Pye said that he himself had recently gone to Oxford with one of the firm's partners to discuss this very matter with Professor Townsend. Appleton commented that this was unnecessary. He, in Cambridge itself, would be very pleased to give the firm any technical advice which they required. Shortly afterwards he became the first technical adviser to what was to become the important Pye group.

In 1924 he was asked to act for Philips in all litigation dealing with the industrially controversial subject of thermionic tubes, while he was soon also acting as physics consultant to Trippe, a decade earlier the RE officer whose illness had launched him into radio. "But I only do this in a way secretly as I do not want it to be much talked about at King's College," he confided to Van der Pol after he had moved to London. "It does not entail much work and has nothing to do with the business side. I just answer the questions they ask me. They do not put my name in any of their publications."

Industrial consultancy was not all. There were frequent consultations with Van der Pol on the book that they were to write together, and Appleton was also considering the idea of a new wireless journal. "The idea ... interests me enormously," he wrote. "I would certainly act as joint editor with someone else. But I could not undertake all the work. I have often discussed it with Watt the meteorologist. You have started the ball rolling and I will roll it further."

He was a good lecturer, confident and unfussy, who knew not only his subject but the best method of delivering what he knew. He had an excellent speaking voice and his early training as a singer enabled him to make himself properly heard. During one period he gave a course of lectures jointly with Rutherford and long remembered how the great man had advised him to get the tricky bits of mathematics down on the blackboard before the lecture began. "If you feel a bit guilty about it," Rutherford added, "tell them you did it to save time. They'll probably believe you."

Together with an effortless delivery very different from that of more than one first-class scientist at the University, there went a strong personal interest in the undergraduates for whom he was responsible. Appleton always felt that to go to a university at all was a great privilege of which the greatest advantage should be taken; every man coming under his care was induced to take it.

K. G. Emeleus has a vivid memory of him during these years. "Once a week," he says, "he saw a group of us who were reading physics for Part II of the Natural Science Tripos. D. R. Hartree and E. G. Dymond were in the group. The University arrangements were poor at that time, and he went to a great deal of trouble to help us, particularly with modern physics, and with basic mathematics in which there was no formal instruction. He was doing some demonstrating for the Part II physics course in the Cavendish Laboratory at that time and, I believe, was also doing some teaching (University or College) in mineralogy. He was not my research supervisor during the next three years when I was in the Cavendish, but I saw a great deal of him, particularly in the latter half of this period. This happened because one of my problems was to find out how the Geiger particle counter worked. Appleton was the Cambridge authority on circuitry and Rutherford suggested that I should consult him. Using the one cathode ray oscilloscope then available in the Cavendish, we (mostly Appleton) established the role of capacity and resistance in the operation of the counter, giving, I think, the first estimate of maximum counting rates. Incidentally, this counter was Geiger's negative point form, not the positive wire form developed later. I followed up this work for about a year and a half on my own." One result was a paper written by Emeleus, Appleton, and M. A. F. Barnett on "Some experiments with an α-particle counter", published in the *Proceedings of the Cambridge Philosophical Society* in 1924.

"Appleton was also interested at that time in the type of atmosphere electricity which C. T. R. Wilson was studying at Cambridge. I once went out with him to see Wilson's apparatus in the field between the Observatory and the Coton footpath. For general interest, I also went to Wilson's postgraduate lectures on this subject. I took down his badly delivered lectures verbatim, when they made sense. When Appleton saw my notes, he told me there was much unpublished research in them, and borrowed (and kept) my notebook."

Another man with a vivid recollection of those days is J. A. Ratcliffe, whose life was to be closely linked with much of Appleton's. "From October 1923 to June 1924, I was reading physics in my final year at Cambridge, and I attended Appleton's lectures on wireless oscillations and waves," he has said. "In these he dealt, amongst other things, with his research interests of non-linear phenomena and atmospherics. At that time, although I was deeply interested in anything to do with physics, I had no knowledge of wireless. I soon found, however, that these lectures made an outstanding appeal to me, partly because, even in those days, Appleton was already the inspiring lecturer many of us knew him to be throughout his life, but mainly because he discussed his subject so broadly that it seemed to embrace a very large part of physical knowledge as we studied it then. We did not seem to be studying "wireless", as it was then called, for its own sake but because it was a subject ideally suited for illustrating and illuminating the whole of physics. It was that breadth which captured my imagination and made me the slave of a subject which now, even more than then, seems to me to be unique in spanning such a wide range of physical knowledge and at the same time impinging so closely on practical engineering matters."

After taking his degree in June 1924, Ratcliffe began to work with Appleton, first on atmospherics. "My business," he has said, "was to observe the direction from which they came. The equipment available was rather primitive. There was an old war-time direction-finding loop and a receiver, and I was asked to go out to Appleton's house to collect the four valves to put into it. I went on my bicycle, but as I left the house Appleton suggested that I had better not cycle back – the valves were too precious, and perhaps I had better walk."

By this time Appleton was on the edge of a career, about to step out into territory he was to make peculiarly his own. He was to devote the rest of his life to its exploration and he was to carry out that exploration, was to deal with his work and his colleagues, very largely in the light of his experience during these immediate post-war years at the Cavendish. Here science was still a matter not for committees but for individuals. "String and sealing wax" was not just a phrase but a method of preparing apparatus, and Rutherford could cheerfully claim: "We've got no money, so we've got to think."

Appleton's beliefs, which were to change little throughout the rest of his life, reflect a good deal of this atmosphere, and it was throughout these years that he formulated his ideas of what really made for good scientific research, of the things that mattered, and of the ways one should go about getting them. "I well remember Marconi telling me that he hadn't much use for theories," he once said with admiration, "... at any rate for those which indicated that this or that was impossible. He wanted to try things out for himself by experiment." Appleton believed that "the big things in science occur when an adventure takes place in the mind of an individual", and he stressed on more than one occasion that "the most important quality a theoretical scientist can have is *imagination*". Like all first-class scientists, Appleton looked on his vocation as creative, as exciting, as a game in which the player was always trying to find out a little more, to push back the frontiers. Not unexpectedly, he found his initial admiration for Rutherford increasing with the years. "If *anyone* knew how to ask Nature the right questions it was Rutherford .... he would say that a man was 'actively engaged in research' or, more colloquially, 'going strong'."

And, like Rutherford, Appleton was a great man for not worrying, usually happy in the belief that most problems would solve themselves if left alone for the right time. There was the occasion when he had persistently failed to get a good vacuum when working in the Cavendish. He left the apparatus and decided to relax with a round of golf. The glass tubing was left in the sun, and on his return he found the vacuum perfect. "Which only goes to show," he would say, "just how important golf can be in scientific research."

CHAPTER 3

1924–1925: DISCOVERING THE IONOSPHERE

BY THE spring of 1924 Appleton was still tied to two lines of research — one dealing with thermionic valves and their non-linear characteristics, the other with the relationship between lightning and wireless atmospherics. Both subjects had great potential as far as the future of radio was concerned, and it is interesting to speculate on what the course of Appleton's life would have been had he remained devoted, even for a few more years, to these two subjects alone. This was not to be the case. Throughout the rest of the year his interests were gradually turned towards something different; and in December there came what was almost a revelation, a series of experiments which convinced him that he had discovered a field of inquiry to which he could devote his life. It is tantalising that after more than 40 years the details of these latter months of 1924 are somewhat blurred, so that in details it is almost impossible to disentangle cause and effect. However, a good deal is known.

In April 1924 there arrived in Cambridge a young man from Rutherford's own country, Miles Barnett, a New Zealander who was attached to the Cavendish as Appleton's research student. Barnett's interest was radio, and one of his first tasks was to record, as accurately as possible, the strength of the radio signals received in Cambridge from 2LO, the broadcasting station which the British Broadcasting Company — as it then was — had opened in London 2 years previously. Appleton himself has stated that he had become interested in this very subject while in the

Royal Engineers. "As a result, after the war, when I returned to Cambridge, I began to work on the subject, starting first to develop more accurate methods of radio signal measurement," he has said. It seems likely, however, that this work had been to some extent pushed into the background. But it was taken up with considerable vigour now that a stimulus was provided by Miles Barnett.

What Appleton and Barnett soon discovered with the relatively primitive apparatus at their disposal was a characteristic which is now familiar but which in the early 1920's still needed experimental investigation: that while the strength of the signals received during the day was constant, this strength varied at night, rising and falling with what were realised to be almost periodic variations. Differing explanations for this could be put forward. The one which attracted Appleton was that at night the Cambridge apparatus was receiving not one wave but two — one which travelled in a direct line between London and Cambridge and another which travelled upwards in the atmosphere and was then reflected downwards, thus reaching the receiver along two sides of a triangle, whereas the other wave followed the third side. In this case, he postulated, interference effects would inevitably produce such a fading. "To explain the Cambridge results," he later wrote, "we must assume two things: first, that the reflected wave is only appreciable at night, and, second, that the nature of the reflection is variable in time. Corresponding results obtained for sending stations at greater distances than London indicated the increased importance of the night-time reflected wave as compared with the direct wave. For example, in the case of continental broadcasting stations, only an extremely weak signal was received during the day-time; but, after sunset, the intensity though variable, increased very greatly in magnitude." This meant, of course, that the constant direct wave was weak by both day and night, and that the strong signals received after sunset were due largely to waves which had taken the overhead path.

All this assumed the existence of a reflecting layer high above the earth, a layer which — if it existed above the rest of the world — would enclose it like a skin. In 1924 scientific opinion on the existence of such an enclosing layer was strongly divided. It had first been postulated

4*

some 40 years previously by Balfour Stewart who suggested that the small daily changes in the earth's magnetic field already discovered might be due to electric currents flowing in the upper atmosphere. Shortly after the turn of the century, the question was given added interest by the work of Marconi who in 1901 succeeded in sending radio signals from Cornwall to Newfoundland. This great technical feat was given the praise which it merited; but it raised what appeared to be an awkward problem. How, it was asked, could the wireless waves "manage to bend round the protuberance of the curved earth"? Why did they not shoot off, as it were, into outer space?

At first it seemed possible that diffraction, that well-known process of bending which was understood in relation to light waves, might be sufficient to take the radio waves round the curvature of the earth— at least the relatively small curvature that was involved in an Atlantic crossing. But even as further research showed this to be impossible, wireless transmissions were being received at far greater distances. Soon there could be no doubt that they were being received on the other side of the earth. However, help was at hand.

In 1902 two men had put forward similar theories which would account for this long-distance reception of radio waves. They suggested the ideas independently, and in this way echoed Darwin and Wallace who both began to work out, quite independently, the groundwork for the origin of species. The leader of the two was Oliver Heaviside, "a somewhat wayward scientific genius" as Appleton once described him, a physicist and electrician who was working in seclusion in Devon, and whose three simple sentences in an *Encyclopaedia Britannica* article contained the nub of the matter. "There may possibly be a sufficiently conducting layer in the upper air," he wrote. "If so, the waves will, so to speak, catch on to it, more or less. Then the guidance will be by the sea on the one side and the upper layer on the other."

A similar idea was proposed by A. E. Kennelly, although he was doubtful whether such a layer would, alone, account for all the reports of long-distance reception, which continued to increase as more and more men began to experiment with the new possibilities of radio. This purely tentative theory was given more substance about a decade later when W. H. Eccles, a radio engineer of note, suggested that the number of ions, or electrically charged atoms, increased with the height of the atmosphere above the earth; if this was so, he postulated, then radio waves passing through these increasingly ionised regions would surely be bent to follow the curvature of the earth.

However, the existence of such a "Heaviside Layer", as it had been christened, still rested on nothing more than theory, and its opponents were tenacious. What is perhaps surprising is that they were able to hang on even after the experiments carried out by a young Marconi engineer, T. L. Eckersley, in 1920, and reported in *The Radio Review* of February and May 1921. These appeared to show that there was reflection from an upper layer by night but not by day, and postulated that the difference was due to the sun's ionising influence. "If the experiments in this paper are considered to be valid, then the existence of a ray reflected at night-time from some upper conducting layer of the atmosphere may be considered to be beyond doubt and the fact that this ray is responsible in part for the errors of night bearings may also be taken as proved," Eckersley concluded in 1920. But there were still doubts about how these characteristics were produced; a long series of letters and contributions to *The Electrician* during the autumn of 1922 showed that Eckersley had, in fact, failed to make his point with many colleagues.

Two years later Appleton entered the scene, and he arrived with an idea of great simplicity; an idea which would not merely show whether the postulated layer existed, but would, if successful, provide the actual height of the layer above the earth. He carried out a few more experiments. Then, in October, he came before the Radio Research Board's Propagation of Waves Committee to explain what he had in mind.

"Professor Appleton described the experiments he had been carrying out at Cambridge with his assistants, on the existence of the Heaviside layer," run the Minutes. "Using a galvanometer in the anode circuit of a valve in which the steady plate current was balanced by potentiometer, he had been observing the relative strength of the field radiated from the London Broadcasting Station. A few minutes after sunset he found that ripples could be detected in the galvanometer reading due, he believed, to interference bands produced by reflection at a conducting layer in the

39

atmosphere. He suggested that if the wavelength emitted could be regularly varied during a short period it would be possible to calculate, from the changes in the interference bands observed, the height of the layer." He was proposing to approach the British Broadcasting Company with a view to asking whether arrangements could be made to alter the wavelength emitted from 2LO by a small amount through a few seconds as required. Should it be found that the Company would be willing to co-operate in these experiments, he asked whether the Committee would recommend that the request for the required transmission might be made officially by the Radio Research Board.

"The Committee expressed great interest in Professor Appleton's work and strongly recommended that the Radio Research Board should co-operate in every possible way in the experiments. The Secretary was instructed to discuss with Professor Appleton and Mr. Hollingworth the possibility of arranging for observations additional to those made at Cambridge."

This formal account is supplemented by a letter which Appleton wrote to Van der Pol a few days later, on 12 October.

"Now for some information which I hope you will keep secret, for I do not want it to get out to any company," he wrote. "We have been measuring the intensity of [2LO] London at Cambridge and get *every night* [there follows a diagram]. In other words indisputable interference bands for the mean night values the same as the day value. Now we should expect upward movement of the layer immediately after sunset and so get interference bands. We are now arranging with the BBC who are intensely interested to alter their [diagram] continuously through 3 metres and we hope to get on our resonance curve and from the No. of maxima we get the height of the Heaviside Layer!!! What do you think of this? We are just making final arrangements for the receiving apparatus and then we are going to try it. If this works we have got really *direct* proof of reflection at last."

On 6 November the Radio Research Board agreed that the necessary equipment should be bought—at a cost which came to about £250. At that time, says O. F. Brown, then the Board's Secretary, "it used to be said in the Civil Service that a paper published by the Royal

Society or the Institution of Electrical Engineers, was good value at £1000." Appleton's £250 was to produce not merely a paper but a new field of science.

However, 2LO could not conveniently change its wavelength, and it was then suggested — whether by the Radio Board or by Appleton is not certain — that the BBC transmitter at Bournemouth might be used. Thus we come to what was not only a crucial experiment in the history of radio but one from which the whole of Appleton's future career was to spring.

His idea was basically simple. The signals broadcast from Bournemouth would be picked up after coming by two different routes, one along the ground and the other after reflection from above. When the difference in length of these two routes was a whole number of wavelengths they would combine to produce a loud signal; when the path difference was equal to an odd number of half-wavelengths the received signals would, as it were, tend to cancel one another out, and the reception would be weak. A simple equation utilising the mean wavelength, the small continuous change in wavelength made by the transmitter, and the number of "fadings" — all of which were of course known — would enable the difference in length of the two routes to be estimated. Since the distance between the transmitter and the receiver would be known, simple triangulation would enable the point of reflection — the top of the triangle — to be found. And the top of the triangle would, of course, represent the height of the Heaviside Layer above the earth.

There was only one minor snag. In order that the difference between the strong and the weak signals should be as great as possible, it was necessary that the strength of the ground wave should be so reduced that it was comparable to the reflected wave. These conditions would be met if the Bournemouth transmissions were received not in Cambridge but somewhere only about half the distance away. Oxford filled the bill, and early in December Appleton's specially built receiving apparatus was installed with the help of E. W. B. Gill in Townsend's Electrical Laboratory at Oxford. Barnett described the necessary choice of Oxford instead of Cambridge as a pity; Appleton commented that most Cambridge men had their Oxford moments.

On 11 December Appleton left Cambridge for Oxford with Barnett. The special transmissions were to start from Bournemouth after the end of the evening's programmes, so that when dinner was over there was time to make final adjustments to the receiver. "And I always thought I liked dance music," commented Barnett as they waited in Townsend's laboratory listening to the last number of the Savoy Orpheans.

Shortly before 12 o'clock, Bournemouth closed down for the night. Over the special telephone link which had been arranged, Captain West, head of the Bournemouth station, told them to be ready. Shortly after midnight the first of the special signals was sent out.

Within literally a few minutes it was clear that Appleton's plan was working.

"Only an ordinary slow-moving galvanometer was used to measure the strength of the current being received," he later said. "Therefore the signal was not varied too rapidly, and natural fading occurred while the fringes were being produced by the comparatively slow wave-length change. But when the results were examined there was no doubt that there were more fades while the wave-length was changing than there were when it was constant, and from the number of these extra fades, or fringes, it was deduced that the reflection had been from a height of about 100 kilometres."

For the first time it seemed to be proved that the Heaviside Layer was really there, an invisible shell surrounding the earth like a ghostly continent but one whose characteristics still remained a mystery.

More than 30 years later, when being interviewed about the results of the International Geophysical Year, Appleton was asked how he had felt on that distant evening in 1924 when the position of the ionised layer above the earth had been pin-pointed for the first time. "Well, of course, it certainly was very exciting when we got our first indication that there was an ionosphere," he said. "But, you know, I think I should say this: that however hard you work at scientific research, there's always a certain amount of luck in it. After all, you know you can't discover something that isn't there, and if there hadn't been an ionosphere, well perhaps I wouldn't have had the pleasure of talking to you as I am now."

The evening's experiment had been a great success. Rutherford, with

Cambridge
2/1/25

My dear Balth,

Many thanks for all your recent communications. I have now started work again after the holidays & this Fire or article _will_ be finished as you shall see!!

First let me answer over two points.

(1) The presents sent by Nettie & yourself are beautiful. Thank you so very much. Nettie must have thought of the railway journeys to London when the scarf will be very comforting. Hugy & Bessie are delighted with their presents and will be ! writing separately

(2) The photograph of the children is very beautiful. The children are very handsome for they are like Nettie — _not_ that they would not have been handsome if they had been like you. I hope you get this very English idiom.

(3) I am sure the Phil. Mag. would be very pleased to have your elegant solution of the old coupled circuit problem but of course the Germans are very keen on this.

(4) The Philips book is very funny. I shall have some lantern slides made of these for my wireless lectures.

(5) I have a lot to tell you about the Heaviside layer & reflection. You need not have returned the MSS but I will send you reprints of my Phys. Soc. article containing the suggestion & worthy short waves are better than long. Larmor has put this suggestion in mathematical form in his Phil. Mag. article & gets that the coefficient of absorption is proportional to the wave. length. All the old work of Watson, Eccles etc on a reflecting layer must be wrong because their results show that there is better reflection for long waves than for short but experimentally it is the reverse.

I told you about the interference bands between direct & indirect ray. Well I think it is alright. I calculated that at about 100 miles from a Station (Broadcasting) the two rays should be of equal amplitude & we should get fading

Fading

and we DO. I went to Oxford to measure Bournemouth & this was the case. Also I got the height of the layer which is however very variable. If we alter the wave-length from say λ_1 to λ_2 (eg from 380 to 390 metres) and D is the path difference

then

$$\frac{D}{\lambda_1} - \frac{D}{\lambda_2} = n\lambda$$

where n is no. of interference bands passed through. We did this (BBC helping) & the resonance curve was not A but B

(A)   (B)

From this the value of D can be calculated & thus the height. Of course all this is unverified at present & in a few weeks time I am going to Oxford to do it again so don't please mention it to anyone. I want to be very cautious because of it is right it proves the existence of the Heaviside layer in a way that has not been done before. Rutherford is delighted. Of course it is the simple but direct kind of expt which appeals to him. The height seems to vary from 50 to 80 kilometres.

If my ideas are right we can measure the height in this way a huge field of investigation is opened up for with an Einthoven we can measure the height at any instant or so get the nature of the movement. Well all this will be very nice and I may be asking you to join with me in some tests from your transmitting station when I am a little surer of my results. Our friend Gill who let me have an aerial at Oxford saw the readings & was convinced it was right. He said he had been shaky about reflection theories till it was proved so directly.

I am very anxious to know what you think

Kind Regards to all

Yours Ever

E.V.A.

P.S. Oh I forgot to tell you of the applause you got at the Phys. Soc. I was speaking of aerials excited at frequencies higher than fundamental in connection with an other successes and I said that it was very remarkable that you had foretold "in the dark ages of wireless" that an aerial of this type would send up waves obliquely to be reflected. At this the company burst into applause.

whose blessing Appleton had been working, was genuinely delighted and described the event at the annual Cavendish dinner a few evenings later — a sign of unusual enthusiasm since "shop" was as a rule avoided on such occasions.

However, it would be wrong to imply that the results of this one evening's work, an evening when man had put out a hand to touch a new fact of Nature for the first time, were to be accepted without question or without doubts and queries being raised. Appleton himself noted, as the experiments continued, that the height of the reflecting layer appeared to be very variable. There was another point. "We were not ... entirely satisfied with the results of this experiment since a sceptical critic could argue that all we had proved was the existence of transmission from sender to receiver by two paths of different length and that both paths might have been situated near ground level," he later wrote in Devil's Advocate fashion. "It was therefore necessary to prove that the longer path had, in fact, been pursued in an overhead fashion."

His attitude is shown in a letter which he wrote to Van der Pol on 2 January 1925, and in which he described the Oxford results. "Of course all this is unverified at present, and in a few weeks time I am going to Oxford to do it again so don't please mention it to anyone. I want to be very cautious, because if it is right it proves the existence of the Heaviside layer in a way that has not been done before. Rutherford is delighted. Of course it is the simple but direct kind of experiment which appeals to him. The height seems to vary from 50 to 80 kilometres. If my ideas are right and we can measure the height in this way a huge field of investigation is opened up, for with an Eindhoven [a more sensitive form of galvanometer] we can measure the height at any instant and so get the nature of the movement. Well all this will be very nice and I may be asking you to join with us in some tests from your transmitting station when I am a little surer of my results."

Some months later he did return to the Townsend Electrical Laboratory; at last he had found a use for Oxford, he would say — a place where Cambridge people could make their crucial experiments. This time the same team simultaneously compared the signal fading variations from Bournemouth on two receivers, one having a loop antenna and the other a vertical antenna. The results from these two sets proved conclusively that among the signals being received were some which came down at a steep angle and which could not possibly have been received as reflection from, for instance, distant hills. Furthermore, the angle at which these reflections were coming to earth tied in with the triangulations by which the height of the Heaviside Layer had been calculated.

More important, the mechanism by which the ionosphere affected radio was now being clarified. "We may imagine, that at night the layer is sufficiently high and intense to permit of ionic deviation taking place, the ray being turned through large angles without undue absorption," Appleton wrote in *Nature*. "During the day the ionisation due to solar agencies throws the ray down at lower levels (for example 40–50 kilometres), and here, although ionic reflection can take place, the collisional 'friction' causes heavy absorption at these short wave-lengths and high grazing angles. The difference in the action of the atmospheric ionisation between day and night is therefore to be taken as due to the differences in height (and therefore density) of the effective layer, and not as due to the difference in sharpness of the boundary of the layer as has been usually assumed."

He was in no doubt of what he had achieved. "But I am writing to give you results of my latest experiment on Heaviside layer," he wrote to Van der Pol. "*I have measured angles at which waves come down.* French tried to do this, sending waves up etc. but was defeated by reflected wave at the ground which makes strongest signal with vertical but not tilted aerial." He went on to describe what he had done, adding that he was to speak about some of his ionospheric work at the British Association, and adding: "You see there is simply heaps to do on scientific side of wireless and I have just planned a lot of experiments on a large scale for Radio Board. We are going to get spectral analysis of Xs as per my unpublished paper, also repeat changes of wave-length experiment for interference bands with Eindhoven recorder to get change and height of layer in a second. So you can guess I am busy as a bee."

Any remaining doubts were now swept away. At least, they were swept away in most places. But as late as 1926 J. E. Taylor, the well-known Post Office electrical engineer, was deploring that "a good deal of time, money, and energy is being wasted on the pursuit of this academic myth, of a useful ionised layer".

However, most scientists did now believe that high above the earth there existed an enclosing shell of atmosphere that was different in some and possibly in many characteristics from the lower atmosphere. The Americans Breit and Tuve, who proved the existence of the Heaviside Layer quite independently, regarded their discovery as of little importance, and it was part of Appleton's genius that he realised, almost instinctively, the possible implications of his discovery. Most of his other work was now dropped, and the two lists in the little note-book he invariably carried, one giving papers published, the other papers in preparation, show that from now onwards he was absorbed in the upper atmosphere to the exclusion of all else.

The prosaic desire to solve the problem presented was one obvious reason. Yet it was not the only reason. Through Appleton's character there ran a strain of the suppressed romantic, a strain that found some consolation for the trials of day-to-day domestic life in the charting of this new continent he had discovered but of whose moving plains and hills and rivers he knew little. Throughout a long life he could always, when personal worries or administrative difficulties became unbearable, "escape into the upper atmosphere" as he described it. Here the scientist and the romantic merged in a way which he suggested, years later, in his Presidential Address to the British Association. "Perhaps the most striking fact about modern science," he said, "is that, like poetry, like philosophy, it reveals depths and mysteries beyond—and, this is important, quite different from—the ordinary matter-of-fact world we are used to. Science has given back to the universe, one might say, that quality of inexhaustible richness and unexpectedness and wonder which at one time it seemed to have taken away from it."

These words were written 30 years on, but it is difficult not to feel that their spirit moved Appleton as, with Barnett, he prepared to publish the results of their work. First there was a note to *Nature*, then a Royal Society paper, which had to be "communicated" by a Fellow. This was to be not Rutherford, as might have been expected, but Sir Joseph Larmor, a Fellow of St. John's like Appleton and a man who had already

Sir Edward Appleton

speculated at length on what the nature of the Heaviside Layer would be if it did in fact exist.

Larmor, in his late sixties and eminent for his conception of matter as consisting entirely of electric particles, had already encouraged the young man. "As an undergraduate student before 1914 I had attended Larmor's lectures in his College," Appleton later said, "but I do not recall having had any conversation with him. But, after the war, I often sat next to him at the College High Table, and it must have been on some such occasion that he encouraged me to tell him something of what I was trying to do in the matter of research; Larmor was by no means a fluent conversationalist and spoke mostly in single sentences or even phrases. But he frequently helped a shy, younger High Table companion with the opening remark: 'And what have you been doing today?' And I can well imagine that it was in reply to such a question that I was led to tell him what I was trying to do about the ionosphere."

In the early autumn of 1924 Appleton had outlined his projected experiments in a note to Larmor, a note returned with the brief comment: "If you can do this it will help much." Sir Joseph's main concern was with the nature of the physical process by means of which the still hypothetical layer might reflect or refract radio waves, and in October 1924, while Appleton was still preparing for his experiments, he described his latest views in a paper read to the Cambridge Philosophical Society on "Why wireless electric rays can bend round the earth". In this he suggested that the effective particles forming the postulated Heaviside Layer were not molecular ions, as Appleton had hitherto imagined, but free electrons. A corollary, which did not appear to be dealt with in the paper, but which Appleton raised in a paper to the Physical Society Symposium the following month, was that if this were so then the whole theory of electric wave propagation in an ionised medium would have to be modified, since the influence of the earth's magnetic field would then have to be taken into consideration.

Shortly afterwards, Appleton mentioned this point to Larmor himself. "His reply," said Appleton years later, "was that he had overlooked the matter entirely; and, because of this, he did not feel he should modify his own draft. He generously suggested that it was for me to take over

46

the development of the new theory as a project of my own." Larmor's exact words, in replying to Appleton's suggestion that he might add a footnote to his own paper, were, Appleton himself remembered: "No, I won't do that. I'll publish my paper; and you can publish another one to show that I am wrong." One result was that Appleton was now directly pointed towards the problem which was to produce his magneto-ionic equation some years later.

All this now combined to produce ample reason for Larmor's intervention. "Mr. Barnett and I were, technically, workers in the Cavendish Laboratory, since I was a member of the teaching staff and he was a physics research student". Appleton has said, "After the paper was written, I felt that I should submit it to the Professor of Physics, Sir Ernest Rutherford, and seek his advice concerning publication. This I did, and was told that he would himself communicate it to the Royal Society. Upon mentioning this to Larmor the same evening, he replied, rather tartly: 'Oh, no, I intend to communicate the paper myself'. Rutherford, with a kindly understanding, retired in the matter."

There was what Appleton calls a postscript to the story. When galley-proofs of the paper arrived, he found that the title, which had probably contained some reference to the Heaviside Layer, had been altered to "On some direct evidence for downward atmospheric reflection of electric rays"—a title which not only showed Larmor's slightly old-fashioned use of the word "rays" but fortuitously helped to camouflage the significance of the experiment.

Appleton's confirmation in 1924 and 1925 that the Heaviside Layer did in fact exist was a beginning rather than an end. It could be assumed, but only assumed, that the layer stretched around the world. But how thick was it? Why did its height appear to vary from day to day and from hour to hour? Was this height the same, or nearly the same, over different parts of the earth's surface? Did its characteristics change from hour to hour, day to day, or season to season? These were only some of the questions which now stood up to be answered, while over them all there loomed the riddle of what part the ionosphere might play in the quickly developing science of radio.

Late in December, Appleton made a note in his diary which at first glance has an historic, not to say ironic, interest. It consists of a single line asking: "Could an aeroplane get us direction of vector?" Now nearly 40 years previously Hertz had shown that radio waves were reflected in much the same way as light rays, and since then there had been many suggestions—a number of which had been patented—for utilising this reflection for various purposes, and at first glance it is tempting to suggest that Appleton also might now have been thinking of using the reflection of radio waves as this was subsequently developed into radar. However, this was not so. "I was working very closely with Appleton at this time and I think the real situation is as follows," says Ratcliffe. "When a wave is coming down at an angle on to the ground one might at first sight think that the direction of its arrival could be discovered by ordinary direction-finding methods. Unfortunately this is not correct because the wave is reflected at the ground and one has to take into account both the arriving wave and the reflected wave. This causes considerable confusion. I think what Appleton was really after was to use an aeroplane to get away from the ground and to avoid this confusion with the reflected wave."

But no such plane was used. Appleton appears to have given the idea no second thought and, with the problem solved early in 1925, turned to the immediate work in hand, to mapping in ever greater detail the structure of the electric shell which enclosed the earth.

This was to be done during the next decade; but from London, not from Cambridge. For during the autumn of 1924—and even before the crucial Bournemouth-to-Oxford experiment had taken place—Appleton had moved to London as Wheatstone Professor at King's College, reputedly the youngest professor in Britain.

CHAPTER 4

1925–1932: "THE YOUNGEST PROFESSOR IN ENGLAND"

"RUTHERFORD'S young men" were certainly sought after in the world of science; nevertheless, Appleton's translation to London was unexpected, a tribute both to his personal drive and to the impression which he made on academic selection boards.

He had, in fact, been trying to leave the Cavendish for at least 2 years, noting to Van der Pol in May 1922 that the Chair of Physics at the Royal Naval College Greenwhich had fallen vacant, and adding: "Rutherford says he does not know whether another professor is to be appointed, but he says that I am the most suitable candidate he knows." Now, 2 years later, he was able to tell his friend that he was at last making a move. "I have been so dissatisfied with myself as a collaborator because of teaching work at the Cavendish that I applied for O. W. Richardson's Chair of Physics and JJ told me an hour ago that I have been appointed. ...Needless to say the work I have done with you has helped enormously!! Shall be able to get at our work now as I shall only have a few hours a week teaching and all my evenings free."

This determination to press on with the serious business of research and to make his mark was vigorously encouraged by Appleton's wife, and it was largely on her ambitious urging that he now determined to build his own house at Potters Bar, then one of the more exclusive outposts to the north of London and, as he wrote to Van der Pol, a site which due to its situation could well be utilised for wireless experiments and the study of thunderstorms. "The house and land is to cost about £2,300 but, although it will leave us with no money afterwards we think it is worth it," he added. The new home, in whose design his wife took a hand, was an ambitious affair with a specially built study for Appleton himself; a nursery for Margery—and later for his younger daughter, Rosalind, born in 1927— two bedrooms, sitting-room, and bathroom for the maids. Its construction certainly stretched Appleton's finances, and he reluctantly found it necessary to turn down his wife's repeated suggestions that the family should invest in a car. One curious fact can perhaps be traced back to the discussions which arose over this much-disputed but for long non-existent motor car. Throughout a long life, Appleton never resumed his war-time driving. When the family did eventually acquire a car in the late 1930's it was his wife or his daughter who drove; and although in his later appointments he could invariably draw on the services of a chauffeur, there were many circumstances in which it was commented upon that Appleton himself never drove.

Appleton took up the Wheatstone Chair in October 1924, but his new house, St. John's, was not ready until the following March. For 6 months he therefore continued to live in Cambridge, travelling up to London three or four times a week, and making preparations for the new work which he was planning. "In my new job," he had written to Van der Pol in September, "I hope to develop a wireless and triode laboratory so that you will visit us and lecture to us there.... As you probably know the salary is £1,000 per year and by examinations etc. I hope to make another £300 so that we shall not starve. Also when I am 60 years of age there will be a pension of £700 per year or a lump sum of £7,000. I wish to develop the atmospheric electricity and wireless side as much as possible and so shall be grateful for ideas and suggestions that you do not wish to carry out for yourself, which will be duly acknowledged. Also I hope to do some further work on gas discharges, particularly from the point of view of oscillations, in which I hope to emphasise as much as possible the ideas and work of Holst and Oesterhaus.... I find that there will be plenty of time for research and as there are plenty of pumps etc. vacuum and valve work will be easy."

This letter shows what Appleton had in mind as he was planning to move to the Wheatstone Chair — an appointment which was taken up partly because, as he put it to Van der Pol, he "was tired of so much teaching at Cambridge and all research there except mine was atomistic". As a result of the experiments in December and the following 2 or 3 months, these plans were virtually abandoned and then replaced by new ones which concentrated Appleton's scientific interests almost exclusively on investigation of the ionosphere. It is true that at King's he encouraged research students in work which was only marginally linked to a probing of the electronic shell which enclosed the earth; but so far as his own work was concerned this now became the object of all human hope and endeavour.

As yet no special name existed for this ionised layer, and it was only later that there arose the probably apocryphal story of two Fellows of the Royal Society going into a meeting with one asking, "What is the ionosphere?" and the other replying, "Something measured at Slough and interpreted by Appleton." Appleton himself later credited Watson-Watt with the christening about 1932, but recent research at the Radio Research Station shows that the word was first used even earlier: by Watson-Watt in the Symons Memorial Lecture of 1929 and in a letter from him to the Secretary of the Radio Research Board written on 8 November 1926. "We have in quite recent years seen the universal adoption of the term 'stratosphere' in lieu of a previously well established misnomer 'Isothermal layer' and the adoption of the companion term 'troposphere' for the 'convection layer'," this went. "The term 'Ionosphere' for the region in which the main characteristic is large-scale ionisation with considerable mean free paths, appears appropriate as an addition to this series."

It was soon clear that if further information about the ionosphere was to be obtained, observations would have to be made over long periods. Neither Appleton nor anyone else yet appreciated the connection between the 11-year cycle of sunspots and the characteristics of the ionosphere. It already seemed likely, however, that these characteristics might vary considerably from one year to the next, and long-term experiments were therefore essential. In addition, observations would have to be carried out not only in Britain, but in as many other parts of the world as was practicable. It could be assumed that the Heaviside Layer enveloped the whole earth, but this was only an assumption, and there was no evidence that its characteristics were the same above the poles, or above the equator, as they were above Britain. Thirdly, it was clear that comparatively large sums of money would be required for what would, ideally, be an international operation.

These points induced Appleton to revise his ideas during the months that followed the December experiment. Long-term work would require something different from the experiments of *ad hoc* teams provided by a university; many of the observations, he foresaw, would be almost routine, and would perhaps be most conveniently handled by a larger, and possibly government organisation. In addition, the whole scale of the operation which he now began to envisage was very different from that of two colleagues almost casually visiting Oxford for a brief reception of radio waves from Bournemouth. A scouting party had proved the existence of a vast new continent; a series of major expeditions would be required to explore and survey it.

It was in this light that Appleton considered the work ahead, and his consideration was reinforced by the break-up of the Cambridge team itself. Ratcliffe remained in Cambridge while Barnett's link was to be broken by a Greenland expedition. One outcome was that the investigation of the ionosphere that now developed did so within what was, for the period, a curious framework.

The basis of almost all work was the transmission of radio signals from one place and their reception elsewhere, and during the decade and a half that remained before the outbreak of the Second World War a variety of sites and a variety of authorities were involved. Appleton stood at the centre of the complex organisation which grew up—formally as the chairman of the Radio Research Board's Propagation of Waves Committee, but more importantly because it was clear that he knew more about the ionosphere than anyone else.

After the first experiments with Bournemouth, an experimental transmitter was built at the National Physical Laboratory at Teddington, and its transmissions received at the Dogsthorpe Station outside Peterborough, a site chosen so that the ground wave would be of roughly the same strength as the down-coming wave. Subsequently it was realised that shorter wavelengths could be utilised, and transmitters much nearer the receiver were then used, first at a King's College out-station in the East End of London and then near Windsor. Reception of the NPL transmissions was started at Slough, a station soon to be under the charge of Watson-Watt; in a small hut erected on the roof of King's College in the London Strand; and at Cambridge. Reception in the Strand was always poor, and in 1933 Appleton was put in charge of the newly opened Halley Stewart Laboratory in Hampstead where reception was comparatively interference-free. In addition, the BBC was frequently co-opted, sending out waves whose frequency was varied, after the public programmes had finished for the night.

All this resulted in a complex inter-linking of responsibilities. The Slough staff were all civil servants although the Station's ionospheric work was virtually controlled by Appleton who was primarily a university professor. The £400-a-year grant which he received went primarily to support the work carried out on university premises, and he himself received no salary for what he did—other than his university stipend. As a further complication, a number of his earlier colleagues, notably Ratcliffe, continued to help with the work even though remaining at Cambridge. All this was amiable enough and Appleton has gone on record as saying that his relations with Watson-Watt at Slough "were close and were also certainly pleasant". However, this intricate intermingling of government and private enterprise, and of the responsibilities and credits which it inevitably entailed, were to have their repercussions a decade later. For it was partly from research into the nature of the ionosphere, carried out in the United States and Germany as well as in Britain, that the smoke drifted upwards to produce the genie of radar.

The first developments followed the decision by the Research Board that it would support further investigations. It was clear that the ionosphere's effect on radio reception began to die out roughly at dawn, and an obvious move was to concentrate operations on this time of day, and to try to discover exactly what happened. For this, the station at Dogsthorpe, outside Peterborough, was taken over by the Board. In April 1925 it agreed that one whole-time and one part-time assistant should help Appleton record there the reception of special transmissions put out by the National Physical Laboratory at Teddington. In addition, galvanometers "should be supplied to six qualified amateurs who should be selected to carry out observations of fading effects". Total support for the entire ionospheric work was roughly £400 a year and 20 years later, when he had become Secretary of the DSIR, Appleton commented: "Since coming to the Department I've looked up the files and discovered that I could have had more money if I'd asked for it. What a pity I didn't know at the time."

An assistant named Brown was now put in charge of the Peterborough site, and lived in one of the wooden huts there while maintaining the equipment in the other. Two or three days a week Barnett would come across to Peterborough from Cambridge—being replaced by Ratcliffe when he went as wireless operator on an expedition to Greenland in 1926. They would all stay in the local hotel, arrange to be awakened some hours before dawn, and would then spend 3 or 4 hours recording reception of the Teddington transmissions. Frequently they would be joined by Appleton, who would enliven the miserable hours before dawn with his anecdotes of the First World War, discuss the latest cricket scores over the special telephone link with the NPL, and keep the assembly awake with constant cups of strong hot tea.

"One of our greatest assets at Dogsthorpe was our technical assistant, Mr. W. C. Brown," Appleton later recalled. "Now Mr. Brown had been a radio operator on board ship in the First World War, and had travelled widely. He had also acquired great skill in producing creature comforts out of thin air. He could produce a cup of hot tea, in the middle of the night, when there was neither tea, nor milk, nor cups. And when Mrs. Brown joined him, as she did from time to time, the most delicious sausage rolls also used to appear, again from nowhere. All the early work on the ionosphere was done on tea and sausage rolls."

The changes of wavelength were made more quickly than had been possible with the Bournemouth equipment, and the artificial oscillation of signal strength would therefore be more clearly distinguished from the natural fading. As Appleton had already forecast in his letters to Van der Pol, the previous slow-moving galvanometer was replaced by an

The Youngest Professor in England

Eindhoven galvanometer, and with this the rapid changes of received signal strength could be recorded photographically. From these records it was quickly clear that the height of the reflecting layer decreased as dawn approached. At the same time the strength of the reflected signal steadily decreased until, usually about an hour after sunrise, the reflected wave became too weak to record.

It appeared that the height of the Heaviside Layer changed just as it was touched by the sun, and in 1927 there came a fortuitous opportunity of confirming this—an eclipse of the sun. On 29 June the moon would pass between the sun and the earth, and for a period its shadow would fall both on the earth and on the ionosphere above the earth—thus cutting off the direct radiations from the sun as they are cut off at sunset. Would the effects on the ionosphere, Appleton wanted to know, be the same as those of sunset and sunrise?

To help in answering this question, the aid of the BBC was invoked, and the Corporation's Chief Engineer, Peter Eckersley—brother of T. L. Eckersley—arranged that special transmissions should take place from the Newcastle and Birmingham stations. Two separate sets of transmissions were required owing to the low angle of the sun at the time of the eclipse—about 5 o'clock in the morning. For this meant that the shadow cast by the moon on the ionosphere—some 100 miles up—would not be directly above the shadow cast by the moon on the earth; in other words, observations would have to be taken at two different places if phenomena experienced in the region of the eclipse at ground level were to be compared with the region of the eclipse in the ionised layer. The result was that Ratcliffe and Brown went to Liverpool University where in the University engineering laboratory they received transmissions from Newcastle during the eclipse at ground level; Appleton and Barnett meanwhile ensconced themselves in the Peterborough receiving station where they prepared to receive transmissions from Birmingham while the moon's shadow was being thrown not on Peterborough but on the ionosphere some 100 miles above the town.

Ships at sea co-operated by limiting their broadcasts to emergency messages and thus keeping the air free from interference. However, an amateur transmitting station near Liverpool continued broadcasting

55

throughout the eclipse and effectively ruined Ratcliffe and Brown's work, so that full comparison between ground and ionospheric conditions was impossible. At Peterborough, however, all went well.

To ensure accurate comparisons with the day of the eclipse, observations were made on the day preceding it and the day after. As expected, these showed the familiar pattern. As sunrise approached, the intensity of the waves reflected from the ionosphere gradually decreased—indicating that the effectiveness of the reflecting layer was being destroyed by the sun's rays. On the early morning of the 29th, observations started at 2 a.m. as they had done the previous day and as they were to start on the 30th. As expected, the intensity of the reflected wave gradually declined and normal daytime conditions were observed. At 5.10, as the shadow of the moon began to pass across the ionosphere above Peterborough, there was a small but sudden rise in the amplitude of the down-coming ray; this grew until its value was finally sixteen times as strong as was normal in daytime. Then, following the end of the eclipse, the reflected waves sank back to their normal strength.

This result, which shows up with quite staggering effect on the graphs which were soon prepared, seemed to indicate quite clearly that when the rays of light from the sun were cut off, the ionising effect was cut off simultaneously. However, that was not all. For during the eclipse the number of "fringes" caused by the alterations in wavelength suggested that the height of the reflecting layer had increased—a supposition that appeared to be confirmed by alterations in the angle at which the reflected waves were received. From these results—and from records of signal strengths from other BBC transmissions made at a number of places throughout the country—Appleton inferred two things. The first was that in this particular instance the interruption of the sun's rays had removed the ionisation in the lower layers of the ionosphere. The second arose from the fact that there was no visible delay in the sun's effect on the ionosphere; in other words, if the height of the reflecting layer changed just at the time of the optical eclipse, then the agency which produced the ionisation travelled from the sun to the earth with the speed of light.

The year following this work on the eclipse, Ditton Park was reorganised into what became the Radio Research Station under Watson-Watt, and soon after this Appleton met for the first time Robert Naismith, the man at Slough mainly responsible for the Station's ionospheric work and a friend of Appleton for the rest of their lives. That their abilities were so complementary was brought out in a letter which Appleton wrote to his friend some years later. "I do feel that together we represent a partnership which has a fine record and that each of us contributes to that partnership something that the other *cannot* contribute," this went. "I am lacking on the experimental side and you are lacking on the scientific side. But we fit very well together and make a good team."

This letter was written in 1945, some 15 years after the start of a collaboration which produced no less than seventeen joint papers, the first of them in the *Proceedings of the Royal Society* in 1932 and the last of them in the *Proceedings of the Physical Society* in 1947. Appleton soon became a constant visitor to Slough, often supervising the actual work of taking observations and constantly conferring with Naismith on the significance of the latest set of readings. Bubbling with enthusiasm, he seemed to be forever on the telephone from London, forever raising new suggestions. "On one occasion," remembers Naismith, "I received from him in a single day three letters and a telegram. Sometimes I would be up all night taking or supervising the readings which were being made, and would then spend most of the following day working them out. A few hours later Appleton would be on the phone: 'Come up to the Athenaeum and we'll talk them over.'"

In the early years it had been essential that the transmitter should be separated from the receiver by a certain minimum distance. When it was possible for this distance to be reduced, it was suggested that an automatic transmitter should be set up near Slough, close enough to be inspected as necessary, and that reception should be monitored in Slough. However, a snag soon arose. Such regular observations would mean an "observatory"; and observatories were outside the province of the Department of Scientific and Industrial Research, being controlled either by the Meteorological Service or by the Astronomer-Royal.

The impediment was eventually, and ingeniously, overcome. All that was required was a transmitter which was small and an aerial that was inconspicuous. As for a site, Naismith's inquiring glance turned towards the broad acres of Windsor Great Park which stretched away to the south of the nearby Thames. In the Park there lay Prince Albert's Workshop, a small building erected on the instructions of the Prince Consort with the idea of providing a place where the young workers on the Windsor Estate could be trained and where, killing a utilitarian bird with a charitable stone, small items of equipment for the Castle could be made or repaired. Here the required transmitter was duly installed. A great deal of care was necessary before approval was obtained, and a member of the Board was allowed to visit the transmitter twice a week — a stipulation which appeared to rule out regular observations. However, a clockwork mechanism attached to the transmitter switched this on at predetermined times each day, thus satisfying both the letter of the law and Appleton's requirements.

The gradual spread of ionospheric observation which took place during the late 1920's and early 1930's, and of which the Windsor Park series formed a part, was the direct outcome of Appleton's experimental proof that the ionosphere existed. It was accompanied by a series of developments in his work which between 1926 and 1932 radically altered both knowledge of the ionosphere and the methods by which it could be investigated. These developments overlapped chronologically, and they were the outcome of work carried out at Slough, at King's College, and at Cambridge, among other places. Appleton realised that the ionosphere would be penetrated by radio waves if the wavelength were short enough. But he also realised that because of the effect of the earth's magnetic field penetration would be at two different frequencies. His magneto-ionic theory was developed so that he could be quite certain as to which of these frequencies should be used in determining the electron concentration in the appropriate layer. And the need for obtaining quick and automatic observation of such "critical frequencies", as they came to be called, induced him to switch from his frequency modulation method to the newer pulse method which had already been devised in the United States. Appleton's interest in the way in which the earth's magnetic field influenced the ions which reflected radio waves high above the earth had been increased by Sir Joseph Larmor's remarks in 1925, and from then onwards the problems involved were never very far from his thoughts. The great Dutch physicist, Hendrik Lorentz, had already worked out the effect of a magnetic field on light rays passing through a material substance, and Appleton now extended Lorentz's results to radio waves passing through the ionised upper atmosphere. The only difference between the two cases, he postulated, was that whereas the ions were free in the upper atmosphere they were bound together in the substances of Lorentz's calculations. Appleton first expounded his views in a paper read to the General Assembly of URSI — the International Scientific Radio Union — at Washington in 1927. Only précis of such papers are published, and it seems that at that date Appleton did not appreciate the full importance of what he had done. He may have been affected by two other factors. When he had begun work he had wasted a couple of months "persistently attempting to track down a missing minus sign"; what he had done was to overlook the fact that Lorentz's theory postulated the positive instead of the negative electron — "a simple error which I would have seen at once if my mind had not been captive to a groove by undue preoccupation". In addition, his initial work had involved mathematical methods which he knew would not be entirely acceptable, and he had then passed over the purely mathematical problem for further work to D. R. Hartree, who had succeeded him as Director of Studies in Physics at St. John's. Whether or not these things combined to make him underestimate his work is not certain; but the Appleton–Hartree equation has remained important. Appleton's theory showed that the reflection of radio waves from the ionosphere would be affected by a process of double refraction. It helped to show that the charges which caused reflection in the ionosphere consisted of free electrons. And it has since been of the greatest use not only in ionospheric work but in the newer realm of plasma physics.

During the experiments, continued with the help of the Radio Research Board, it was sometimes found that in addition to the main echoes from the ionosphere there were what appeared to be subsidiary echoes, suggesting at first a double reflection from the layer above. However, it soon became clear that these secondary echoes were, in fact, the echoes from waves which had penetrated the Heaviside Layer and were being reflected back from a layer high above it. A height which varied between 90 and 130 km had regularly been found for the main layer. But heights of an entirely different order, varying from about 250 to about 350 km, were frequently measured during the 3 hours before dawn.

"On such occasions," Appleton wrote in *Nature*, "after the high values have been recorded for two or three hours, a discontinuity in the series of values occurs 30 to 40 minutes before the sunrise, and heights of the normal value are again recorded. The experimental evidence, the detailed discussion of which will appear shortly, leaves little doubt that on such occasions, in the period before dawn, the ionisation in the Kennelly–Heaviside Layer has been sufficiently reduced by recombination to permit of its penetration by waves of (400 metres). Reflection, however, takes place at an upper layer which is richer in ionisation. With the advent of sunrise at a height of 100 km or so, the Kennelly–Heaviside Layer is formed again and deviation by the lower layer is suddenly established, the normal fall of the under boundary of the latter proceeding afterwards as the more direct solar influence increases the region ionised. As the day further proceeds, the experimental results suggest that another region of ionisation is formed below the Kennelly-Heaviside Layer, which, while causing attenuation of the waves, does not very materially affect the height at which they are deviated."

In other words, the earth was enclosed not merely with the Heaviside Layer but with a second and outer "shell". Moreover, the Heaviside Layer itself now appeared to be not a static barrier of electrified atmosphere but an almost fluid barrier which expanded and contracted, broke up into two separate layers at times, and was obviously of considerably more complex character than had yet been appreciated.

Appleton soon found not only that shorter wavelengths were reflected back from the newly discovered upper layer throughout the day as well as the night, but that they were reflected back with comparatively great strength. "The more I discovered about this upper layer," he later said, "the more *certain* I became that it was the agency responsible for reflecting short-waves to great distances in practical radio-communication."

One problem that now faced him was that of naming the different layers which together made up the ionosphere. In his early papers he had called the Heaviside Layer the E-Layer, using E in his diagrams and text to indicate the strength of the electric field. Now, finding a layer above, he called it the F-Layer. This, as he pointed out, left the way clear for the naming of further layers lower down – such as the D-Layer which at times was shed, as it were, by the E-Layer—and for the names of more than twenty layers higher up, if these should be found to exist. "I didn't use the letters A, B or C," he once said, "because I felt I must leave a letter or two in case someone discovered other layers below the D-Layer. They haven't done so, so it now looks a bit off to start with the D-Layer. However I admit it's my fault."

Within the next few years, as the morphology of the ionosphere was revealed in ever greater detail, the complexity of electrical shells surrounding the world was increasingly appreciated, and the known layers were divided and subdivided, the F-Layer, for instance, soon being split into F_1 and F_2. Yet for many this upper layer remained only one thing—the Appleton Layer.

Appleton now began to use progressively shorter wavelengths in his sounding of the ionosphere. What he discovered was that by using these shorter wavelengths the periods throughout the 24 hours during which transmissions would penetrate the lower layer but would be reflected by the upper one, were considerably increased. He soon realised, moreover, that the critical frequency, the frequency at which a radio wave would just break through the Heaviside Layer, would give a measure of the electron concentration in that layer at that moment. In other words, his radio probing could be used as a tool to discover the composition of any particular layer of the ionosphere at any particular time under any particular set of conditions.

At first, using the frequency-modulation method, it was found possible to fix the critical frequency only once an hour, but even with this limitation a great deal of information about the upper atmosphere could be collected. "A recent twenty-four hour run using this method has shown that for a mid-winter day over southern England the value of N reaches 2.0×10^5 electrons per c.c. at noon, after which the value falls steadily and remains at the low value of 3×10^4 during the greater part of the night," he wrote in *Nature*. "About half an hour before sunrise a very sharp increase is noted, after which the ionisation increases more gradually until the maximum midday value is again reached. The noon value of ionisation is thus found to be more than six times the midnight value."

Two decades later, lecturing in Edinburgh and explaining how he and

61

his workers had estimated that the electron population of the Heaviside Layer in full daylight was about one million per cubic centimetre, he was able to add a footnote: "Although the first measurements of this kind were made in South-East England as far back as 1930, it is only recently that there has been any check on their accuracy," he said. "Last year, some American scientists managed to send rockets up into the ionosphere and, with automatic equipment attached to the rocket, were able to make some measurements of the density of the electron population at different heights there. The results confirmed completely the results of our radio soundings. I mentioned this recently to a Norwegian ionospheric colleague, saying how happy I was to hear of the agreement between the two sets of observations," he went on. "His reply was, 'Oh, I think it merely proves that the rockets have been there!' "

One important result of the need to discover at frequent intervals the critical frequency at which transmissions would break through the E-Layer was that Appleton now began to adopt the new method of probing the ionosphere already devised in the United States by Breit and Tuve. The frequency-modulation method demanded rhythmical changing of the frequency, and the estimation of the differences of path taken by the direct wave and the reflected wave. The pulse method involved something basically simpler: in this, short sharp bursts of radio waves were emitted and their return from the ionosphere was detected. A direct measurement of the time taken for the double journey out to and back from the ionosphere then gave the height of the reflecting layer—much as the distance of a high cliff can be estimated by a seaman who notes the time taken by the sound from his ship's foghorn to reach the cliff and return to the ship.

Appleton had been considering the use of this pulse method for some time, and had already contemplated a way of overcoming one of its main drawbacks. This drawback was that due to a variety of technical reasons the pulses were of comparatively long duration; this meant that when the distances being measured were relatively short, the pulses—and their returning echoes—could overlap, thus making it difficult or impossible to identify individual pulses and thus fouling up the whole experiment.

This problem was overcome by "squegging". "I think the circuit itself was known even in the First World War," Appleton later said, "but I think I recognised this particular usefulness of it for producing short radio pulses." The device itself consisted of an oscillator in which the oscillations took place in very short spurts until stopped by a negative grid; then the grid charge would leak away through a high resistance leak and the oscillations would recommence – "so that," as Appleton put it, "the time between these two adjacent periods when the oscillation takes place is determined by the time constant, that is, the time required for the charge on this [the] condenser to leak through the high resistance and allow the thing to begin again."

Appleton's first squegger circuit was set up in King's East London College, with the receiver in his hut on the roof of the Strand building. Pulses as short as one-fifth of a millisecond were produced very satisfactorily, and within little more than a year he had virtually abandoned the frequency-modulation method of probing the ionosphere. "So far as I was concerned," he later said, "the most exciting thing we did with it was to discover what we called the splitting of echoes due to the existence of the earth's magnetic field." What he had postulated in theory a few years earlier was now being illustrated in practice.

However, a far more practical result of his switch to pulses was that the long series of research students who came to Appleton at King's between 1930 and 1936 – when he returned to Cambridge – were all imbued with "pulse-mindedness". Many of them came from the Commonwealth and they returned familiar with the techniques of the pulse-transmitter and pulse-receiver to which many had made their own individual contributions; and many of them became, within a decade, leaders of the radar teams which sprang up throughout the world – for the pulse technique was to lie at the very heart of British radar as it was developed by Watson-Watt and his teams from 1935 onwards.

The development of ionospheric investigation during this period was therefore to be of critical importance to the war that now lay only a decade ahead. But it was to be important for more than its development of the techniques to be used in radar. During the war, short-wave radio communication was to become an essential sinew for the conduct of many operations; such communication depended for its efficiency very largely on how much the authorities concerned knew about the state of the ionosphere.

This knowledge was to be supplemented, during the next few years, by two things among others. One was Appleton's work in Norway, which related magnetic storms to short-wave radio blackouts, better known as polar blackouts. The other was his continuing work with Naismith which linked electron concentration with the appearance of sunspots. This work was continued throughout a complete 11-year sunspot cycle, and revealed long-term changes in atmospheric conditions which were of great practical importance since they showed that the range of short wavelengths available for long-distance broadcasts increased very substantially with solar activity. In crude terms, this work helped to give Britain a slight lead in knowing what wavelengths would be most suitable, on any particular occasion, for short-wave long-distance broadcasts. Thus it was possible for Allied forces to be receiving constant intelligence while their opponents were blacked out.

This ever-widening exploration of the ionosphere provided the background to virtually all Appleton's scientific work at King's. When this was not directed purely to finding out more about the ionosphere itself, it was usually concerned with matters directly linked to the problems involved. Within a few months of leaving Cambridge he was followed to London by K. G. Emeleus, who had become one of his junior demonstrators. Appleton gave him space in his own laboratory, encouraged him in his work, and also asked him to help in a number of experiments, one of which, a development of C. T. R. Wilson's work at Cambridge, consisted of trying to measure the currents which would discharge into the air vertically, in a vertical electric field, from the tips of blades of grass grown in the laboratory.

In one of his reports to the Radio Research Board, Appleton gave a good example of how his laboratory work linked up with the larger work of ionospheric exploration. "These," he wrote of experiments on ionised air, "have been directed towards elucidating, as far as is possible in the laboratory, certain properties of an ionised medium which are of importance in theories of radio-transmission. Measurements of the frequency of electron collisions with air molecules at different pressures are being made by two methods. (The electron collision frequency is the factor which determines the absorption of wireless waves in their transit through an ionised medium). In the first series of observations the two methods were found to give different absolute values although the same type of variation with pressure was found. An attempt is being made to find the source of this discrepancy. The air pressure at which maximum absorption of high-frequency energy takes place has been studied with special reference to the influence of an imposed magnetic field. The results have been found to be in complete agreement with predictions from the magneto-ionic theory and thus show that the ideas of R. A. Heising concerning the height of the atmosphere at which the maximum absorption of wireless waves takes place require very radical revision."

This work, utilising in the laboratory a scaled-down version of the ionosphere in an attempt to discover how it worked, was described by Appleton in a number of papers and reports. Like everything that he wrote, they were of great clarity. More than 30 years later he held up a paper on the same subject with the words: "Why can't they write plainly? Why can't they say what I said in 1929?"

In all this work two features were prominent. One was Appleton's comparative lack of interest in experimental apparatus—a trait which was to affect his life in one very significant aspect a few years later; the other was the wholehearted and successful way in which he encouraged the theoretical work of his research students, imbuing them with his own enthusiasms and making them "pulse-minded", "ionosphere-minded", or, perhaps more important, seized with the joy of discovering new facts about the natural world.

His personal laboratory technician was a young man called Gander who, in the words of one research student of the time, "seemed to be able to turn his hand to anything Appleton wanted constructed or got up in the way of apparatus". But once the apparatus had been made, Appleton was concerned with only two things—the results that could be obtained from it and the extent of their reliability or accuracy. "His interest was not mainly in equipment and when it was, he preferred simple equipment," says one of his colleagues. "He would be interested in the working limit-ations rather than the mechanics of the equipment. The squegging oscillator was a typical Appleton device." Once everything was working that was enough for him. Then he could devote his mind to the important business of elucidating what the results produced by the apparatus really meant.

In this process of elucidation he utilised his research students, as well as his staff, so that all appeared to be working together as a team. A good example was provided by W. R. Piggott, a young man who was taught by Appleton at King's, who followed him to Cambridge in 1936, and whose work in this field so increased that in 1960 Appleton could write that Piggott had "played a substantial part in British work on the ionosphere over the last one and a half decades". During the early 1930's Appleton spotted Piggott's abilities, drew him into much of his work, and later put the matter illuminatingly. "In any work we did together, Piggott's contribution was both important and essential. I will illustrate this by reference to the work on ionospheric absorption. Here I formulated the basic principle of the method and made a first very rough series of seasonal noon measurements. This was all very primitive. Piggott then designed proper apparatus and worked out all the operating procedure."

Appleton's ability to give research students and undergraduates this personal involvement in their work was one reason for his success at King's. Two others were the ease with which he handled the administrative load, and his knowledge of how the scientific establishment really worked.

He tackled the administrative part of his duties in a methodical way which even today would hardly be considered normal for a scientist; 40 years ago it was considered much less so. Scientists may not always be absent-minded; but they even more rarely display the unruffled calm of the born administrator. Appleton was the exception, and rather surprisingly so in view of his lack of experience.

"For the first four months," he once said to a colleague at King's, "I studied how the machine worked; after that I could delegate as I wished." And he was able to ensure that while the routine professorial work was carried out properly it yet occupied the minimum time—much as Sir Thomas Holland, the Rector of Imperial College, used to boast that he ran the College on 20 minutes a day.

PLATE 1. Edward Appleton, aged about 16, with his mother, father, and younger sister Isabel.

PLATE 2.   A group of Hanson Senior boys in 1911
with Edward Appleton top left.

PLATE 3.   The Bethesda Church Choir outing to Patterdale in the Lake District.
Edward Appleton left centre, holding straw hat.

PLATE 4. In the Physics Laboratory at Hanson School.

The Youngest Professor in England

Yet while Appleton could arouse in his students a genuine interest in the pursuit of knowledge for its own sake, he also made it clear that this alone might not bring the expected awards. One student who first went into industry and then took up a Fellowship was later asked by Appleton whether he had published anything. "Yes," he replied, "some papers solo, some joint."

"Oh, then that's all right," said Appleton. "It's always as well to have published some joint work or *they* will say you can't co-operate, and something solo or *they* will say you have no originality." Then he asked whether the man had a Ph.D. On being told "no", he commented: "I should recommend you to take one. You can do it by sending in published papers; they will hold it against you if you haven't got it."

"Later," said the recipient of the good advice, "when I heard what *they* said about colleagues who had not Ph.D.s, I was indeed thankful for that advice, and I have quoted it to students for 30-odd years."

This common-sense estimation of how scientists could win friends and influence people was typical of the Appleton of the early 1930's. The man who had located the ionosphere by an experiment of almost classic simplicity was also the university professor with one of the best lecture room performances in London, the urbane scientist who was a counsel's ideal special witness, and whose careful dress suggested the City broker or the local bank manager. He was now on the verge of two events which were greatly to affect his life—a journey to northern Norway which was to enhance greatly his knowledge of the ionosphere, and a move, on his return from Norway, to the Halley Stewart Laboratory which was about to be opened by King's College. What sort of a man was he, as distinct from scientist? How was it that his influence stretched out as, in retrospect, it is seen to have stretched out, beyond the normal province of a university professor?

The second of the questions is the more easy to answer. For while Appleton's speciality was at first glance of solely academic importance, it was in fact closely connected with one of the most important business and commercial features of the inter-war years—the growth of the wireless industry. As the post-war radio boom spread across Britain it became clear that problems of adequate reception in various parts of the country, of interference between one programme and another, of the wavelengths on which transmissions could best be made, were all closely linked with the effects of the ionosphere. What had at first appeared to be a subject for erudite and leisurely examination was now seen to be a vital factor in the development of an industrial empire. There were, moreover, the implications of wireless in the Services, soon to be of increasing importance as Hitler rose to power. And, already available in embryonic form in both the United States and Britain, there was radar, only awaiting the Air Ministry's starting-gun.

All this had strengthened Appleton's contacts with the British Broadcasting Corporation—contacts which were to last a lifetime and to be of increasing importance. The first of these cannot be identified, but he appears to have been in touch with the Marconi organisation at Chelmsford which ran the predecessor of the BBC, and it was widely rumoured that he was offered the post of Chief Engineer to the Corporation when this was set up in 1923. He was a friend of Peter Eckersley, who became the Corporation's first Chief Engineer, and a continuing acquaintance—a more accurate word than "friend"—of Peter Eckersley's brother, T. L. Eckersley. His links with the Corporation were continuous from the days of the early ionospheric work, and the light that this threw on the problem of fading came just as the Corporation was planning regional broadcasting. When in 1927 a BBC Committee was set up under Dr. Eccles to study plans for the erection of high-power regional stations, Appleton was thus made a member. It is clear from the minutes of the Technical Committee on the Proposed Regional Scheme, which met regularly from the summer of 1927 until December 1929, that his advice was important, and he was later made a member of the Technical Committee which considered amendments to the scheme in 1933.

Television was about to be born, and when the BBC began broadcasting the Baird 30-line system as an experimental service—the first of its kind in the world—Appleton's advice was again sought. "I well remember telling Baird," he later recalled, "that I was expecting two pictures to be received—one above the other—at places on the edge of the service area. This was due to the action of the Heaviside Layer which caused a second picture to arrive at the receiver a little later than the main one which had travelled along the ground. Eventually I received a drawing from a Bristol viewer of a man with two heads one above the other—and from the displacement I was able to get a nice determination of the height of the Heaviside Layer. *I* got excited about all this but I naturally didn't find Baird sharing my enthusiasm at all!"

These growing links with industry, and with a powerful government corporation, helped to give Appleton a standing outside the scientific world as well as inside it. So did his growing work for individual companies—and the fact that on 21 November 1927 he became adviser to *The Times* on wireless subjects, an appointment he was to hold until he went to the DSIR early in 1939. Not that his scientific standing had fallen behind; indeed, his work on the ionosphere had brought him the Fellowship of the Royal Society in 1927, at what was then the comparatively early age of 35.

This honour coincided with another disagreement with Van der Pol which threatened, for a while, to divert Appleton from his single-minded concentration on the ionosphere. "My dear Balth," he wrote on 10 February 1927, "Mr. Ratcliffe has drawn my attention to certain points in your *Phil. Mag.* which refer to me and which are likely to do me a lot of harm. I helped you with the relaxation-oscillation paper translation and wish you had asked me to do the same, for then I should have seen the references to myself. I know, of course, that you meant me no harm, but anyone reading the article would think that all the work of my synchronisation paper was stolen. It is unfortunate that this should come at this time as the Royal Society election takes place in a few weeks." He suggested that an error in dates was at the root of the matter, and he went into the matter in detail. "I cannot, of course, write to the *Phil. Mag.* and point all this out, especially as the paper is written by a friend, but I must try to put matters right in a future paper. I have, of course, so much work in hand in connection with the upper atmosphere that I intended to leave the non-linear problems entirely to you, but now I have taken them up afresh." He went on to point out that the first work on non-linear problems had been contained in the Fellowship thesis which he, Appleton, had submitted in August 1919, and added: "As I say, I had definitely decided to leave all the non-linear problems to you because I have so much

Heaviside layer work to write up, but now I have decided to publish a lot of things I did years ago, both experimental and theoretical, so that I may have a few opportunities of putting matters straight."

Van der Pol replied comfortingly, pointing out that he had no wish to harm his friend but adding that he considered it quite unnecessary to put matters right; perhaps Appleton had magnified the potential damage due to his natural concern about the Royal Society election. Appleton himself later wrote that he was "now inclined" to let the matter drop—although adding that "in the interests of truth it is well to remember that my Fellowship thesis of 1919 dealt with the non-linear problem of oscillation". His feelings had no doubt been genuinely influenced by the fortuitous timing of Van der Pol's paper, for before the end of February he was able to write: "You will be glad to hear that your reference to me has not affected things, and that I was elected FRS last Thursday for my work on atmospherics and Heaviside Layer."

There were 150 candidates that year. Only fifteen were to be elected, and Appleton was uncertain of what the outcome would be. When the news came in the form of congratulatory telegrams—"Rutherford's was the first so it is the historic one," he wrote to his relatives in Bradford—he was alone in the house with his 6-year-old daughter and excitedly went out into the garden to tell her. "I was," she remembers, "quite unimpressed!"

The strength of his feeling is shown in the letter to Bradford, commenting that the Potters Bar Post Office wondered what was happening, that telegrams were still arriving, and that those which he enclosed were only a few among many. "As you know," he went on, "the F.R.S. is the highest scientific honour there is, much higher than a Cambridge Fellowship. It is remarkable that as yet I have had no letter from Palmer at Cambridge. We ran neck and neck in the Tripos, and he got his John's Fellowship before I did because he did not join the Army. However I have beaten him at the last lap." Strictly speaking, he added, he would only be a Fellow after the election ceremony, when his correct title would then be "Professor E. V. Appleton, MA, DSC, FRS".

The letter was typical of many in which Appleton recounted to his family the more interesting or newsworthy events of his life. Thus the

70

visit of the Duke and Duchess of York to King's College, where he had
shown them some of the laboratories, was followed by a letter giving
details of the news reels in which the incident would be contained.
"Everything went off well," he added. "The Duke and Duchess were just
delightful and I had nearly half an hour chatting with them and showing
them round. After that we had tea with them. The Duchess liked the funny
things best. I think the enclosed cuttings, which please return, will tell you
all about it.

"I will send you any photographs I can get hold of".

"We went to the Centenary dinner afterwards and sat down with
quite a crowd of people. But I think we both found it rather dull—especially the speeches. It was, however, a good dinner—the food I mean."

Such letters provided an illustration both of his wish to underline that
his parents' sacrifices had been worth while and of an innocent pride that
he had progressed from the back streets of Bradford to the rooms of the
Royal Society. A curiously similar spirit had been shown 70 years previously by T. H. Huxley, that giant of giants, who on being elected to the
Society's Council at the age of 27 had written to his old biologist friend,
William MacLeay: "When I last wrote I was but at the edge of the crush
at the pit-door of this great fools' theatre—now I have worked my way
into it and through it, and am, I hope, not far from the check-takers."
Appleton felt much the same.

Although the Methodist covering of his youth was beginning to wear
off, by these middle years of his life he still retained an undogmatic Christian faith. He continued to believe in God, and his elder daughter has a
vivid memory of how, during one Isle of Man holiday, her kite landed in
a cornfield. Her father said that she must not try to get it back, as this
would destroy the corn; so the girl gave a last despairing pull and up
came the kite into the air once again. The explanation, said Appleton,
was that God had given it back to her since she had been considerate to
the farmer. If he wore such beliefs lightly, they nevertheless remained—
held in place partly by the views of his wife, who was known to forbid his
colleagues to discuss science on Sunday.

It was as a physicist that he had made his mark not only in science but
in that border country between science and industry. Yet he was already,

at this point in mid-life, feet firmly on the ladder, oddly different, not only from the popular image of the scientist but also from the reality. There were few men less like the common caricature of the other-worldly professor than the careful and methodical Appleton, lecture notes always well arranged, diary in good order, always on time, the man who never missed a train or an appointment. Yet he was different also from the aloof men to whom science spoke in a personal secret voice. While Rutherford saw science as a great adventure, and Einstein knew it to be a mystery, Appleton, almost alone among his contemporaries, succeeded in making it homely. It was this homeliness, evident even in the laboratory or on the lecture platform, which he carried almost as a non-scientific quality into his everyday life. In many ways he did look, with his sober tidy clothes, his stiff collar, and his bowler hat, like the thousands of common-place City gentlemen whose life was lived not amid science but on a routine nine to six chore of office life. Yet it was not only the physical appearance – not even his keen and growing interest in the stock market – which resulted in three City brokers mistaking him for one of themselves in a Liverpool Street to Cambridge train, an incident which he retailed with glee. His beliefs, his interests, were very comparable.

His hobbies were of the happy, undemanding, conventional sort – golf, his garden, musical evenings, and help with the amateur theatricals of his wife, who brought the members of the Potters Bar Women's Institute Dramatic Society to rehearse in the large square rooms of "St. John's". On Sunday afternoons he would wheel out in the push-chair his younger daughter, Rosalind, accompanied by her sister Margery, who would bring food for the ducks on the local ponds and for the horses in the fields they passed in their walk. On Saturday mornings he would play golf, a game for which his enthusiasm continued to increase – so much so that when he returned to Cambridge in 1936 he was almost childishly delighted to learn that Bernard Darwin had once stayed in the house he rented and had actually practised putting on the lawn.

"When I used to play a lot I wasn't very good at skill," he later remembered, "but I was a jolly sight worse at character. I was quite hopeless at what I may call 'ordeal by bunker'. If I missed a ball first time in a bunker I hit it hard three times, which at least gave me the satisfaction that nobody else ever played with it again. But, alas, I was told that that counted four strokes in all. The only way I could get my score down on a card was to use an indiarubber. If I went round the course on my own I could always do a 72, which illustrates the bit I mentioned about character." His performance can rarely have been as bad as this suggests, since on at least one occasion he returned home with a large silver cup with a golfer on top.

One reason which Appleton gave for the size of his Potters Bar house was that the Van der Pols would be able to stay with them whenever they wished. This hope was not fulfilled, but other guests were numerous, and Appleton was widely known as a generous host. He himself enjoyed the good things of life with a Yorkshire gusto—good food, good wine, good books, and good music. The gardening in which he took a personal interest would invariably produce far more vegetables than the Appleton family needed—and the surplus was distributed not as separate items but by the armful. In much the same way he would never buy his children less than half a pound of sweets at a time; such favours were bestowed "wholesale", without much thought, because it was part of his nature to act that way. Whenever he was travelling and noticed a particularly attractive box of handkerchiefs or chocolates he would buy it and send it off to his mother—one of his "unbirthday presents" as he called them.

He was generous, too, in other ways, and one instance of his generosity of spirit was long remembered by his elder daughter Margery. "It was when I went to see the results of my Matriculation exam," she says. "I was never academically brilliant and the result was very much in question; luckily I had scraped through, and as I came up the path to the front door, it opened and a hand bearing a box of chocolates was extended round it *before* I announced the results. How touched I was—and how happy to have good news."

Across this happy story, in which hard work had won brilliant recognition, there now began to grow a shadow which it is impossible to ignore in any serious account of Appleton's life and work. "From 1927 onwards," says Margery, "life became progressively unhappy for us all, due to my mother's increasingly difficult temperament." The exact cause of the trouble was never to be discovered; but more than 30 years later Lady Apple-

73

ton—as she had by that time become—suffered a serious stroke, and there are some indications that the trouble had begun many years previously. This would have been a purely personal matter but for the circumstances. Appleton hated a quarrelsome atmosphere. He hated to argue. High on his priority list was a quiet life. One result was that in the years ahead he was increasingly driven in on himself, to that world of the upper atmosphere over which he held undisputed sway. From the early 1930's onwards he found, more and more frequently, the need to take out his little black book of calculations and, as he put it, to "escape up into the ionosphere".

CHAPTER 5

1932–1936: NORWAY AND THE HALLEY STEWART

APPLETON's progress upward in the scientific hierarchy, and his development as a human being, moved on without interruption, year by year, decade by decade, the result of the gradual accretion of knowledge and experience rather than of any cataclysmic experience. In 1932 there came, however, a journey that in some ways marked a watershed in his life, an expedition to northern Norway that underlined the position he had already achieved and also, by a stroke of luck, brought him to the right spot at the right time so that he, the scientist best fitted for the task, could make another important contribution to man's knowledge of the ionosphere.

His leadership of this expedition, a British contribution to the International Polar Year of 1932–3, was largely the result of the position he was already acquiring in the international field. The start of this had been in 1927 when he had attended, in Washington, the second General Assembly of URSI whose President he was later to be for 18 years and whose work he was to influence for even longer. URSI had been set up in 1913 to encourage international study of scientific radio — only a few years after Marconi's historic experiments but at a time when it was already clear that international co-operation would be needed for the most efficient development of the art.

In 1927 Appleton had read two papers to the Washington Assembly — one dealing with the existence of more than one ionised layer in the upper atmosphere, and the other giving a summary of his newly developed magneto-ionic theory. However, he had also mixed well with other members of the Union; he had boundless energy and an awareness of the international nature of fundamental research; he seemed, moreover, willing to cut his leisure and devote the hours saved to the time-consuming business of committee work. The following year, therefore, he was chosen as successor to W. H. Eccles, chairman of the Union's Committee on Atmospheric Disturbances, one of the numerous groups which were kept permanently in existence to review developments in separate specialised radio fields.

This was a useful move up the spiral for a young man still in his middle thirties. Another was to follow 3 years later. In 1931 the Fourth General Assembly of URSI met in Copenhagen. Many of its discussions were attended by Dr. La Cour, the Danish physicist who was President of the International Polar Year Committee, and who was already deep in its work. The First Polar Year had been held in 1882. The second was to begin exactly 50 years later at midnight on 1 August 1932 and had the same simple aims as the first. Existing meteorological and magnetic stations in high latitudes were to be reinforced by temporary stations so that the north polar region was ringed by observers in Siberia, Canada, Greenland, Spitzbergen, and Norway. Records would be taken throughout the year, and from these the effect of polar conditions on the different branches of geophysics would be studied, and their effect on the rest of the world would subsequently be deduced. At a meeting of one URSI group – that dealing with radio wave propagation – Dr. La Cour suggested the formation of a URSI Polar Year Sub-commission which should organise scientific radio observations on an international basis during the coming year. The young Appleton was already a member of a purely British committee which had been set up within the Polar Year organisation to carry out radio investigations, and he was now made chairman of this URSI Sub-commission, other members being Dr. La Cour, Commandant R. Bureau, his old friend Van der Pol, and his old acquaintance Watson-Watt. From this point onwards Appleton was therefore to be wearing two hats – one as a member of the purely British group dealing with the Polar Year in general, and the other as the head of an international body dealing with radio. The experience was to be invaluable.

The main outcome of the deliberations which now began was a British decision to send a small party to northern Norway specifically to carry out observations on the character and behaviour of the ionosphere at high latitudes.

"Tromso was chosen for our observations because of the facilities which the Nordlys-observariet here provides," Appleton wrote. "When I first thought of making upper-atmosphere observations at a higher latitude I had thought of Hammerfest because Dr. Searle of Cambridge had told me of the amenities there, and Dr. G. C. Simpson has already used that town for his atmospheric-electricity work. It was at the URSI meeting in Copenhagen that Dr. La Cour of the Copenhagen meteorological observatory first suggested Tromso. He pointed out that while there was very little difference between the latitudes of Tromso and Hammerfest, the former had the advantage of observatory facilities. The British delegation to the URSI Conference immediately decided to propose to the British National Committee that one of Great Britain's contributions to the work of the International Polar Year 1932–3 should be the sending out of a party to Tromso. Other countries appeared willing to co-operate by sending out similar expeditions and then the whole of the wireless work during the Polar Year was started. (Perhaps I should not have said 'the whole' here, because naturally the meteorological stations are usually equipped with wireless apparatus; I mean here special investigations in which ionospheric work is the central feature)."

The British National Committee decided that the Radio Research Station should be asked to carry out the observations, and Naismith was suddenly informed one morning that he had been earmarked as a member of an Arctic expedition. The others were to be Appleton himself, W. C. Brown, by this time a member of the Slough staff, and G. Builder, a young Australian who was carrying out postgraduate research under Appleton at King's College. The plan was that all four men should go to Norway, and that Appleton should return with one of the party after a few weeks. The remaining two men would stay for the rest of the year to carry out somewhat routine observations, while Appleton would return for a short period towards the end of the Polar Year.

The first task was to prepare the necessary apparatus. This included a pulse-sender which was to be set up on the island of Simavik, some 20 miles from Tromso, and a receiver and polarimeter for use in the Tromso observatory. In addition there was to be a short-wave sender for communication between Tromso and Slough and a 10-metre pulse sender which was to be operated at Tromso for special observational work at Slough. Money was short, a good deal of improvisation was called for, and most of the equipment was made at the Radio Research Station itself. One of the key items was the high-power transmitter. Naismith succeeded in borrowing a number of naval valves for this and hoped that it could be built by the GPO. The GPO reported that the job would take 2 years even if carried out by a large firm. Eventually, the transmitter was made at Slough in a matter of months; it was, moreover, to have a distinguished life, since after its return to Slough, still operating without trouble, it was taken by Watson-Watt to Orfordness on the Suffolk coast and played a part in the development of radar during the years immediately before the outbreak of war.

There was also the cathode ray equipment. The early ionospheric work had been carried out with the help of an Eindhoven string galvanometer which produced a photographic record. This had begun to be replaced by cathode ray equipment in which reception was shown by a blob of light on the tube—the famous blips of early radar—and in the cathode ray oscillograph this was recorded automatically on photographic paper. Arrangements had even to be made with the manufacturers to produce an emulsion specially sensitive to the blue colour of the light on the cathode ray tubes. While this innovation had many advantages, it was more expensive, more complicated, and more liable to breakdown, and Appleton himself was critical. "The Polar Year ionospheric expedition to Tromso was hampered and to some extent frustrated for the whole year by lack of funds because of their exhaustion in building and supplying the necessary auxiliary equipment to go with the cathode tubes," he wrote later. "Many of the first measurements of the expedition were lost due entirely to faulty cathode ray oscillographic equipment. . . . The expedition was saved by the willing sacrifice of its members, often at great personal inconvenience and by the thorough knowledge of our subject so that we were able to make up for what must otherwise be regarded as a too early change-over to the use of cathode ray tubes even in 1932." In addition devices to ensure that the pulses emitted by the transmitter were synchronised with the cathode ray equipment 20 miles away had to be developed, and special types of radio receivers to ensure an absence of distortion in the recorded pulses had to be constructed, as well as all the power supplies and much auxiliary equipment.

The expedition left England on 9 July, sailing from Newcastle for Bergen with twenty-six packing cases of equipment and a specially protected case of valves which Appleton brought up with him on the train from London. The journey was uneventful, first to Bergen, and then in a local steamer which took the party up the indented coastline, calling at Aalesund, Mold, and Bodo, and arriving after 4 days at Tromso, whose observatory was run by Dr. Harang, a Norwegian who was to remain a close friend of Appleton until the latter's death more than 30 years later. Here the real work began.

"The observatory is on the hillside and over a mile from the centre of the town – a real stiff climb up winding streets and lanes," Appleton wrote. "We first went up to make its acquaintance and to ask the people there if they would telephone for us to a carrier to take the huge cases up from the quay. This was done and so we went down again to the quay to see the stuff loaded. The cars, which were like sleighs in shape, but had wheels, were pulled up by ponies. We then went up again to see the stuff taken off and to follow the waggons to see that nothing happened to the glass ware. Then down the hill again to *middag*, which is lunch and really the chief meal of the day. This was from 2 to 4 pm which is the usual time here. Well, then we went up again and at 4.30 began our unpacking. We were five in all, our own party and the instrument-maker at the observatory. We worked solidly for four hours with only a break for some coffee and got practically everything unpacked. It was a big job and apart from directing the aerials at Simavik, where the transmitter is, I guess it will be our hardest manual job."

On the Monday – after the expected day's rest on Sunday – the aerials were erected, and on the following day Naismith and Brown set off with the remaining ten cases of equipment for Simavik, the township and island 20 miles further up the coast. By the time that Appleton and Builder arrived two days later on the bleak low-lying island, the transmitting station had been erected. The aerial masts, each consisting of two stripped larch trees strapped together by iron clamps, still lay on the ground, since the few inches of soil which was all that lay above the bare rock was insufficient to support them.

"We had long discussions with the Chief Engineer at Simavik and the linesmen working there (using our bit of Norwegian, their bit of English, actions and diagrams)," Appleton reported back to England. "Cement foundations according to them, meant waiting eight days for setting, and for a time this amount of waiting appeared inevitable. Finally, we decided to wrap our wire for the stay-loops round big boulders buried in the ground. The Chief Engineer and the other local people assured us that this would be more than satisfactory even with the high winds they get there in winter. So it was a case of pick and shovel all the day but with the help of local labour (1 man all the day and 2 men for an hour or so each), we got up both masts and by 11.30 pm we had our aerial up too." Everyone gave a hand. "We are quite sure," Naismith wrote later, "that Professor Appleton's colleagues in England would not have recognised him that day in the guise of a true British workman, wielding a pick and shovel and hauling on the end of a rope."

With both transmitter and receiver in working shape, there now followed a week of testing, of running-in the apparatus, and of making final commissariat arrangements for the member of the expedition who was to spend a year on the island, broken by only occasional visits to the—comparatively—high life of Tromso. "We have worked solidly since landing a week ago (with the exception of Sunday) and now we have established communication with the Simavik station," Appleton wrote from Tromso at the end of it. "We obtained our echoes nicely and have already found that there are both reflecting regions (upper and lower) here just as there are in England."

Another week's work followed, much of it routine since, as Appleton wrote back to England, they were "settling down to steady work. It is a case of up to the Observatory in the morning; down to *middag* for 2 pm, up again at 4 pm and down again at 8 pm. By 9 pm I am ready for some theoretical work or writing of some kind and bed at 11 or 12 pm." Somewhere among the "writing" was the regular daily jotting of his doings that he sent back home—addressing this alternately to his family in London and his parents and his sister Dorothy in Yorkshire.

Interspersed with the work of setting up the rest of the apparatus was the task of accepting friendly Norwegian hospitality, both from those in Tromso itself and from the family at Simavik with whom Brown would be staying for a year and who made a celebratory visit to the town. A lunch that started at 2 p.m. and was still continuing four hours afterwards; a journey round the neighbouring countryside in a car holding ten, "one sitting on the mudguard", during which three bottles of brandy and many of beer were consumed; and continuous calls to the Englishmen to "come round for drink"—these were only part of the hospitality. Appleton and Naismith, overwhelmed, eventually sought refuge in the local cinema, leaving the gay round to Brown and Builder.

Meanwhile, the final work of preparation continued, and on the 27th Appleton wrote that he was very tired as he had been up to the observatory three times during the day. "That means three hours walking," he added. "Our days are the same now, but we are seeing the end of the purely physical work. Today we put up the aerial with which we hope to get into communication with England and short waves. Meanwhile, I have been using all odd moments filling our batteries with acid. I must have filled 500 so far. All the time we have signals from our main station at Simavik going, and so are sending out waves on which we observe the echoes. So you see we are not wasting time. By the end of the week, and therefore with a fortnight's work in all, we shall have all our apparatus fully working. That won't be a bad record I think. I feel fairly sure that we are going to be able to carry out our main programme."

This main programme was, of course, to start with the commencement of the Polar Year at midnight on 1 August. Less than two days later, the team was to make its first major set of readings, over a 24-hour period starting at 5 p.m. local time on 3 August.

In some respects Appleton, like Napoleon's more fortunate generals, was lucky. He had been attracted to radio at a time when it stood on the verge of great development and exploitation. He had seized on the ionosphere and made its study peculiarly his own just at the moment when

81

such study had the maximum impact on world communications. Now he was to be lucky again.

In the late afternoon of 3 August Appleton again went up to the observatory above Tromso. Brown and Builder were by this time back at Simavik, and exactly at 5 p.m. they were to start transmission. Appleton would record reception throughout the night, until 8 a.m.; then he would be relieved by Naismith who, in turn, would carry on until the end of the 24-hour period at 5 p.m. It was still bright daylight, and it would continue to remain light until well past midnight as Appleton, armed with chocolate and cigarettes for the lonely vigil, made himself coffee.

It is pertinent to remember here exactly what the four men would be doing. On Simavik, Brown and Builder would be sending out radio waves much as the BBC's Bournemouth station had been sending them out eight years previously during Appleton's initial experiments. But more was now known about the invisible curtain of the ionosphere which curved above the earth. It was known that while transmissions on some wavelengths would burst right through the different curtains or layers which Appleton had by this time shown to exist, certain wavelengths would be reflected from the E- and F-Layers respectively. When these critical wavelengths were discovered—and it was known that they varied with time all over the world and in different parts of the world—transmissions made on wavelengths near to them would be reflected down and these echoes would then provide the information for estimating the height and density and thickness of each individual layer.

At 5 p.m. the transmissions began. Appleton was in touch with Builder and Brown by a separate two-way radio, and after a number of routine adjustments it was found that 83 metres was under existing conditions the critical wavelength for the E-Layer. All seemed to be going reasonably normally.

Then, at 10 p.m., virtually without warning, the signals coming down from the ionosphere failed to appear. "I was astounded," Appleton later recorded, "to get absolutely not the slightest sign of an echo on a range of wavelengths from 500 metres to 30 metres. . . . Good echoes had been obtained previously. Such a 'blot-out' was unparalleled in my experience previously."

Then, after two hours, the curtain above the earth began to make its existence felt once again, but with characteristics that Appleton could not understand. "After a while I got signs of reflection of a very weak echo from what, from eye-estimation, I gathered to be an abnormally low E region. . . . After a few hours, signs of echoes appeared, but conditions were disturbed all throughout the run, for we kept frequently getting the absence of echoes. Moreover when echoes appeared they were sometimes in positions on the cathode ray tube which corresponded neither to E or F regions." Then at 4.30 there came another "blot-out" — Appleton's word for what is now known as a polar blackout.

Reception was coming back to normal when Naismith arrived to take over at 8 a.m. But, as Appleton wrote, "all this seemed very mysterious".

The solution came more quickly than might have been anticipated. As Appleton "went off duty", he chanced to meet one of the Norwegian assistants at the observatory. "I think we should have seen the Northern Lights last night if it had been winter," said the man. And he then drew Appleton's attention to the routine magnetic record taken by the observatory, a record that as Appleton remembered it later was still wet from the dark-room. This record showed that a severe magnetic storm had started at about 9.30 on the evening of the 3rd. The mechanics of the storm's operations were unclear; but it did appear so to have affected the ionosphere as to black out any radio transmissions which relied on this reflecting curtain for their journey round the world — a factor which was to become of crucial importance to both sides in the war which was now only seven years away.

At first the connection between radio reception, a hole in the ionosphere, and a magnetic storm, was, of course, only an assumption, but it was one which Appleton was naturally determined to follow up as is made clear from a series of entries in this journal. After recording the night's events, he goes on: "I determined to have a talk with Director Harang about storms and got some very interesting data. The storms here tend to come on successive nights. For example, he said that after a fairly quiet period we got this storm at 2120 and that it should occur at about the same time (or with regular shift) for a few nights. This is going to be very interesting for us, for it means that we can do a continuous run over these nights. Certainly this looks like a kind of 'hosepipe' effect that reaches the earth on the dark side. Perhaps other polar stations get this same effect with a lag in time. I was also told that the magnetic field produced by a storm was always such as would be caused by a current flowing around the auroral zone. I take this to be a ring with the magnetic pole as its centre. Apparently Birkeland saw this clearly many years ago. Also it is found that August–September are the times for storms and February the quiet part of the year. . . . "

Then, four days later, he records: "10 August, 1932. . . . The storm which gave us such an interesting result on the first international test, 3–4 August, showed itself for a few nights at about the same time. The effect got gradually weaker and by now it is practically gone. I am hoping that by these continuous runs from 0800 to midnight we shall be catching another and so be able to get a closer correlation in time. . . . "

Three more entries illustrate how he had become fascinated by what was to be the most important phenomenon to be revealed by the expedition.

"13 August 1932. . . . The evening runs have continued, each taking a turn. I had mine last night and had the interesting reduction of echo amplitude which I think means a magnetic storm. But we do not know yet, as the records are not yet developed. I hardly think that the case of our first test in E Region can have been fortuitous. Tonight Naismith is to observe and perhaps he may get an effect at the same time. It is very curious that here the storms occur usually during the night and usually before midnight. . . . "

"14th August, 1932. Naismith reports that last night he had the same reduction of echo intensity to zero, the value of the amplitude of the reflected wave coming down to at least 1/50 of its previous value. Director Harang, whom I saw this morning, reports that he himself developed the records of the last few nights and noted that storms had taken place. We must examine these more carefully tomorrow."

"17th August, 1932. I have now examined the records and find that the correlation with the storms is by no means so marked. That is to say, that we obtained our blot-out of echoes actually before the main magnetic disturbance. The storms all had their maximum magnetic effect about midnight whereas we got our absence of echoes as early as 2144. However, it is fairly clear that the storms may cause the absence (of echoes before the appearance of magnetic effects). It is a pity that we did not go on further but of course we did not know what was happening in the world magnetic. This all points to our having continuous records during the night on a single wavelength as well as P'f curves as frequently as possible. For example, after a storm is found on a certain night, it is pretty certain to recur at about the same time (on following nights). This has proved the case in the last group. The evenings of 14/15 August and 15/16 August have proved fairly quiet. It is however curious that we only get the blot-out on a night when there is, or is to be, a storm. This effect can hardly be fortuitous. But I am not yet an expert in reading the magnetic records properly."

Throughout the first 3 weeks of August, Appleton and Naismith continued to organise the regular taking of the ionospheric soundings that was to continue for a year. Appleton had to ensure, as best he could, that there would be no hitch in local supplies throughout the long, dark winter, that interruption of communications with England would be avoided, that difficulties with equipment could be dealt with without too much delay, that the small lonely outpost would run itself, do its job, and bring back the expected mass of data in due course.

He himself did a lot of the donkey work, and in helping to arrange for supplies made one remark that was, whatever his scientific eminence, to ensure his fame throughout much of Norway. Dictionary in hand, he was asking about supplies of goat's-milk cheese and failed to understand the roars of laughter. Then it was explained to him that billy-goats could not provide cheese. The scarcity of Englishmen in northern Norway, the aura of local fame which surrounded the party, no doubt helped to explain the spread of the somewhat trifling story. But almost 30 years later Appleton, by then Principal and Vice-Chancellor of Edinburgh University, was invited to a semi-official cocktail party at which he was introduced by his hostess to a huge Norwegian surgeon. "Ah," said the visitor, with remembrance in his voice, "Appleton—the mad English scientist who wanted billy-goat cheese."

Eventually, all preparations for the coming year's work were complete,

Sir Edward Appleton

and on 21 August Appleton could write in his diary: "The work at Tromso is now well in hand and Naismith and I feel we can leave." There were convivial parting celebrations and then the two men left their colleagues to continue the work of the expedition. "So here I am back safe and sound and quite pleased with what we've done," he concluded in his journal. "I've brought back the first set of records and will have the others sent back to me each week. Now for a bit of a holiday."

The records, of course, were what mattered. In this respect ionospheric work, with its massive accumulations of data on whose interpretation advance rests, has much in common with genetics, where the clue to discovery can be provided by the facts collected throughout generations. The records which were to be provided by Simavik were enormous, and to help in their handling a special assistant was taken on by Appleton to help at Slough, the Miss Ingram with whom he and Naismith were to collaborate throughout the next few years.

Appleton himself went back to Norway the following summer and visited the party still collecting data on Simavik. He knew that not everything was well. "We have now only one old transmitting valve left," he reported to Watson-Watt on 8 May 1933 before he left England. "With this Brown is trying to keep the station working but it requires constant adjustment. The number 2 transmitter is therefore stopped and the Germans (who had also sent a team to Norway as part of the Polar Year investigations) have therefore no Transmissions from us as I am now doing all the recording on No. 1 transmitter so long as it lasts." Appleton appears to have believed, possibly with justification, that too great a jump forward had been made in planning the expedition's equipment. He felt much the same, though with no cause, when the same Watson-Watt was developing radar defences five years later.

So far as Appleton was concerned, the work of the Second Polar Year spread out far beyond his own return to Britain, beyond the return of Naismith and Brown from northern Norway in the autumn of 1933. With Naismith and Builder he produced for *Nature* a preliminary account of "Ionospheric investigations in high latitudes late in 1933". He lectured on the radio work of the Polar Year to the Royal Institution. With Miss Ingram he wrote in 1935 a report for *Nature* on magnetic storms

86

and upper atmosphere ionisation. It was only two years later, however, in 1937, that he produced with Naismith and Miss Ingram what was to become the classic Royal Society paper, "British radio observations during the Second International Polar Year 1932–1933".

Appleton had his fair share of credit for what was a successful expedition. But other men were also involved, including above all Watson-Watt who had organised the equipment end of the expedition as superintendent at Slough. Appleton's reaction was epitomised in a letter to Naismith. "When you come to look at things fairly and squarely it simply amounts to this," he said. "If the expedition had turned out a frost I should have had to bear the whole burden of the blame on my shoulders. Now that it is a success there are other people who want to share in it!"

Scientifically, Appleton's work in Tromso and Simavik showed the existence of polar radio blackouts and provided much information on their mechanism. This was important in itself, but more was to follow. For the effects of magnetic storms on the ionosphere were subsequently to be traced down from the Arctic to the Equator, where their effect was different from that at higher latitudes. In temperate latitudes the storms tended to eliminate the electrons in the upper atmosphere – and therefore to interrupt short-wave radio links. But over the Equator the same disturbance had the effect of building up the electron densities in the upper layers of the ionosphere, and thereby actually improving short-wave radio links. The impact on radio communications was, of course, to be immense; for while London–New York channels might be blacked out by magnetic storms it might yet be possible to send messages to a station on the Equator that would then relay them back to a station in temperate latitudes – information which was to gain added importance during the Second World War.

In a way totally different from all this, and one which was just as important as far as Appleton's career was to be concerned, the expedition to Norway, and the results which it provided, established his position among the international radio experts whose work and influence was on the edge of great expansion.

Soon after his return from Norway in the late summer of 1932 Appleton moved from "St. John's" at Potters Bar to a new home in the spacious upper floors of 30 Chesterford Gardens, a large house in Hampstead. This had been given to King's College by Sir Halley Stewart and in May 1933 was formally opened by Rutherford as the Halley Stewart Laboratory.

From his first days at King's, Appleton had been short of space, even though he had doubled the available area in the teaching laboratory by building a mezzanine. Much work had to be carried on in the basements of the Strand building, while his radio work had been forced into the roof-top hut not only because this was scientifically convenient but because there was nowhere else to go. In addition, the growth of radio during the later 1920's had increased the problems of interference with the ionospheric work, and the transfer of this to the heights of Hampstead meant that it could be carried on, as Appleton put it in a progress report to the Radio Research Board, "under greatly improved reception conditions". There was, in addition, a great advantage in Appleton living "on the site". As Rutherford put it when he formally opened the laboratory, "even if the experiments require occasionally that night should be turned into day, the work of Professor Appleton and his staff can be carried out under the pleasantest conditions".

The move, which enabled him to sell the Potters Bar house, was timely, for although he was by this time augmenting his King's College salary with advisory work, there were many calls on his finances, apart from those of a growing family. Thus in 1929 the firm for which his father worked closed down and Peter Appleton soon found himself among the two million-odd unemployed. In addition he was ill. Edward Appleton marshalled his resources, made a number of calculations, then moved his parents into a new home, and made provision for them for as long as he was alive and earning.

The Halley Stewart laboratory occupied the ground and first floors of 30 Chesterford Gardens. Appleton and his family lived on the floors above, and there is little doubt that the 4 years which he spent there with his wife and two young daughters were among the happiest of his life. The deterioration in his wife's health was as yet no more than troublesome. His two daughters, Margery in her early teens and Rosalind aged 5 on his return from Norway, added a family gaiety to the house. The students who came to Hampstead regularly, and who frequently sat throughout the night at the receivers, logging the echoes from the ionosphere, seemed like friendly junior colleagues. And, of course, most important of all, Appleton was now even more deeply committed to his exploration of the upper atmosphere, a lifetime's work that had grown into a near obsession. "I once thought of taking up chess," he said of this period. "Some friends tried to teach me. But I was put off it by one thing: it would, I saw, merely take away time from my study of the ionosphere."

Appleton's students and collaborators during this period included E. C. Bowen, who was to play such an important part in the development of shortwave radar during the war; the Roy Piggott of whom Appleton later wrote that he had "been outstandingly successful in linking up the scientific exploration of the ionosphere, by vertical incidence sounding, with the practical employment of the ionosphere, as a reflecting mechanism, in long distance radio-communication"; and D. B. Boohariwalla, who 30 years later wrote revealingly of how he remembered the Halley Stewart.

"There was no colour bar in his home," he said. "We did our research work at the Laboratory, we cooked our lunches there, which Professor Appleton encouraged, and in the evenings we played games in which Professor Appleton and Margery joined us while Mrs. Appleton and Rosalind looked on. It was such a glorious time I had."

The play—frequently table tennis—was a regular feature of Appleton's instruction, and students were not encouraged to join his group unless they learned the game. For one thing, he would explain, it encouraged them to mix together and get to know one another. In addition, it enabled them to break out of the over-serious mould that might otherwise cripple their work. "How long have you been thinking about it?" would be a favourite inquiry when he found a student brooding over a problem. "Why not drop it and come and have a game?"

He was insistent on students not only understanding what they were doing, and why, but also on their being able to explain it to others.

Every week he would therefore hold a discussion group, taking the chair himself on alternate weeks and on the others insisting that it was taken by one of the students.

Three main lines of investigation were pursued at the Halley Stewart: ionospheric measurements which were in effect a development of Appleton's earlier experiments aimed at determining at specific times the height and ionisation-content of the various layers; the study of electrical field changes due to lightning flashes, a direct continuation of the earlier work done with Watson-Watt; and laboratory experiments on the high-frequency properties of ionised air, an attempt to discover in the laboratory some indication of how the ionosphere might do its work above the earth.

Much of the routine observation, the reception of signals transmitted either from Slough or from King's College in the Strand, would be carried out by research students. There was always a midday run of observations and, once or twice a week, a 24-hour run consisting of two 12-hour shifts. Sometimes the students would be joined by Appleton, returned from an evening meeting, from one of those official or formal dinners for which he was in demand as a speaker, or from a quiet chat at the Athenaeum in whose long upper library he would discuss informally, with a member of the Radio Board, a friend in the BBC, or a high civil servant, those connections between the ionosphere and the long-range radio reception which was with the growth of the Empire services of growing importance even in these pre-war years.

However late the hour, Appleton would invariably sit himself down with the men at the receiver. There would usually be a call for strong, hot tea. And then, for an hour or so, sometimes into the early morning, he would stay commenting on the data that came in, reminiscing about the early days at Cambridge or Dogsthorpe, only a decade away measured in years but another world as far as knowledge of the ionosphere was concerned. And more than once the reception, the characteristics of the tiny points of light on the cathode ray tube, would be affected by the echoes from a plane flying over London, interrupting the radio waves being sent up from the Strand and bounced back to the Halley Stewart from the ionosphere, a fact of life which then appeared—as it had done

PLATE 5. Graduation Day, Cambridge, 1914.

PLATE 6. Newly commissioned at Aldershot in
1915, with unidentified fellow-officer.

PLATE 7.   Physics Research Students of the Cavendish, March 1919. Edward Appleton, centre back row with Sir J. J. Thomson, centre front row, and C. T. R. Wilson on his left. Van der Pol second from left, back row (*by courtesy of Hill & Saunders*).

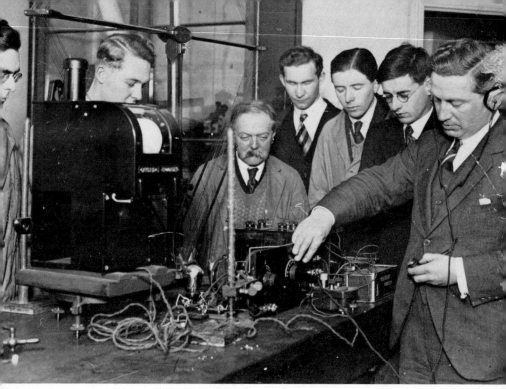

PLATE 8.   The young professor, far right, at King's College, Strand
(*by courtesy of* Camera Portraits).

to Post Office operators noting the same thing—as inconvenient rather than significant.

During this intensely active period of Appleton's life, pure ionospheric research was far from being his only interest even if it was his main one. He was, of course, continuously involved with the BBC on the development of regional broadcasting, while it was with his encouragement that J. L. Baird gave his first ultra-short-wave transmission of television. "In 1932," Baird has written, "we were doing experiments with ultra-short waves, and I remember discussing this while lunching with Professor [Sir Edward] Appleton. He stressed the importance of this work very strongly and advised me to push ahead and give a demonstration at the earliest possible moment, so that on 29 April we gave a demonstration from the ultra-short-wave transmitter at Long Acre, the image being received on a thirty-line television receiver on the roof of Selfridges."

In addition to this involvement with the BBC, official and unofficial, Appleton was now becoming much sought after as an expert witness in the various legal cases which trailed in the wake of broadcasting's advance. A good deal of his work at King's and the Halley Stewart was carried on with the help of "bits" cannibalised from radio sets given to him by firms for whom he acted, and the extent to which this work cut into his time is shown by a letter to Naismith written in the summer of 1933. "I am sorry I have been so long answering your letter, but this legal case has kept my nose down," he said. "It has been great fun, though, and I've learned a lot. It is the Franklin reaction patent, and Marconi's have sued Philips. We were 13 days in the court and now I am helping the judge with the judgement which he reserved."

Appleton also squeezed in time to act as external examiner for more than one university. He was apt to be recalled, decades later, as a person rather than a professor. "I think you were the only External Examiner whom the children remembered," wrote the wife of his host when he examined for Dublin University, ". . . not, alas! for your attainments but because you could swallow a knife." In Belfast, "he endeared himself to my family when he stayed with us, with conjuring tricks and by his natural kindness", wrote his former colleague, K. G. Emeleus. In Birmingham he stayed with a dour Scot, Professor S. W. J. Smith, who would round up his research students or staff and invite them to his home to play tennis or engage Sir Edward in conversation. "Those invited," recalls one of the young men involved, "were specially urged to think up, or search for, conundrums or puzzles or knotty problems to present to Sir Edward who always arrived with some of his own. It was his custom to offer one or more to Professor Smith after dinner. Whilst the Professor struggled with the problem, Sir Edward would play the piano. He was very fond of playing the *Moonlight Sonata*, alleging that this would soothe the Professor if he should get into difficulties."

It was a full and satisfying life, with the Halley Stewart his own near-private empire, a long line of successful research students to look back on, and many more to come, with a growing position in the field of international radio. But now, after a dozen years in London, Appleton prepared to move again.

CHAPTER 6

1936–1938: THE BIRTH OF DEFENCE SCIENCE

IN 1934 C. T. R. Wilson, Appleton's Cambridge colleague of an earlier decade, resigned from the University's Jacksonian Chair of Natural Philosophy whose incumbent had to pay particular attention "to that opprobrium medicorum called the gout" and who had also to produce an annual document, signed by at least eight scholars who could certify that they had attended his lectures. There was a lapse of a year, but early in 1936 Appleton was appointed to the chair after negotiations with the University on the continuation of his ionospheric work.

This work was by now exceedingly well organised at the Halley Stewart, and at first glance it seems strange that Appleton should have been willing to uproot the plant he had cultivated there over the last few years and risk the problems, if not the dangers, of a transplant to Cambridge. However, he was to be attached to the Cavendish; before his move he had persuaded the University to build him a field laboratory on the Madingley Road; and he was quickly to be re-elected a Fellow of St. John's. All this weighed heavily with Appleton, for whom Cambridge had always been the promised land. Even so, there was some speculation at the time, some surprise at the move. Appleton himself has left no record which casts light on his decision; and he would rarely discuss personal motives with his colleagues, who tended to remain acquaintances rather than to become close friends. There is no certainty, therefore, that the idea of one day succeeding to the Cavendish Chair passed through his mind. However, more than one colleague took this for granted, and years earlier, soon after his return to Cambridge from the war, he had outlined to at least one colleague his plans for first gaining a London appointment and then returning to Cambridge to run the Cavendish. Appleton was not the sort of man to wait for dead men's shoes; yet he must have realised that Rutherford, by then aged 65, might well retire in a decade or so; and unless he had an unduly pessimistic view of his own future he must have realised that by 1946 he would be well placed to succeed him. As a single item in the pattern of Appleton's moves, perhaps not too much should be made of this; yet if his life is to be regarded not as that of a bloodless scientist but as that of a human being, it would be unwise to ignore it.

When Appleton moved to Cambridge in 1936 he went fully prepared. He had already gained support from the Radio Board for the transfer of his work from the Halley Stewart, and approval from them for a six-point programme that included a continuation of virtually all the experiments he had been carrying out. He took with him his Halley Stewart laboratory assistant, Peter Roberts, and a number of his research students, including W. R. Piggott. In some ways, therefore, the move was merely one of location. The Wheatstone Professor had been translated into the Jacksonian Professor — but the investigation of the ionosphere was to be pushed on much as before.

It was now, soon after his arrival in Cambridge, that Appleton decided to investigate one possible link between geomagnetic and ionospheric phenomena. He knew that the direction of the compass needle was subject to two sets of movements which appeared to correspond to two tidal motions in the height of the ionosphere — one linked to the sun and the other to the moon. "It was just a hunch of mine that they might be detectable," he wrote some years later to Lawrence Bragg, "and Kenneth Weekes did the careful measurements and dived vigorously into the statistical theory which had to be applied before we could be sure that the effect was real...."

It was first necessary to discover the height of the E-Layer with far greater accuracy than before, since it was realised that the fluctuations would be relatively small, and to the Cavendish Field Laboratory — the

Appleton Hut as it was soon known—there was now brought an electric differential circuit of great delicacy built by Piggott. For many months, pulsed signals were sent up from the grounds of the Solar Physics Laboratory about 200 yards to the north; they were received in the Appleton Hut on the new equipment and it was now discovered that the height of the E-Layer could be pin-pointed at any moment with an accuracy of about 500 yards. When Weekes's careful measurements were statistically broken down one thing became clear—that there was, as Appleton had suspected, a regular lunar tide as well as a solar one, with the height of the E-Layer rising and falling with the passage of the moon over a distance of about a kilometre and attaining its maxima about 45 minutes before the lunar transits. Thus to the already complicated characteristics of the ionosphere there was now added one more.

Appleton had settled himself back into Cambridge very satisfactorily. As Britain's leading ionospheric expert, he was not merely a Professor at the Cavendish, but an ornament to the laboratory, a figure in the long line that went back past Rutherford and J. J. Thomson to Clerk Maxwell. At St. John's, where it would be true to say that he not only enjoyed but venerated the solid evidence of successful learning accumulated through the ages, he held stimulating discussion meetings in his rooms, lectured to the College scientific societies, and in his Fellow's set of rooms overlooking the river installed early TV equipment on which his research students could watch the Boat Race. From his family house in the Madingley Road he planned the court and patent work that now came to him in some volume, marking individual briefs in his diary with figures that ran into hundreds.

In the autumn of 1937 more work was put on him. Rutherford was taken ill. He had been in his normally good health and was expected to recover quickly from the operation which was found to be necessary. The reverse was the case. Rutherford died in October. Appleton became Acting Director of the Laboratory, and throughout the winter of 1937 and the spring of 1938 carried the weight of the laboratory's administrative work.

Much now rested on the appointment to the Cavendish Chair, that key post in the British scientific hierarchy. It is by no means clear that

Appleton expected it, let alone hoped for it; but it would have been beyond the bounds of human nature had he not seen himself as ideally fitted for it. Among those who remember the situation of three decades ago there is a difference of opinion as to Appleton's position in the list of "possibles"; to some he was near the top while to others this was inconceivable. Whatever the betting in Cambridge, there was some surprise when the decision was announced in the summer of 1938 – for the simple reason that the man picked to be Rutherford's successor was still settling himself into another important post to which he had gone barely a year before. Appleton himself must have received the news with mixed feelings. For coming to rule the Cavendish there was now his old colleague Lawrence Bragg, appointed Director of the National Physical Laboratory only the previous year, only 2 years older than Appleton, only 1 year ahead as a research student in the previous decade, the already distinguished son of a distinguished father, and now leap-frogged up two rungs of the ladder in little more than 12 months.

Whatever Appleton's personal feelings in the late summer of 1938, they were overshadowed by the demands of the times. For Britain was now slithering down the slope towards the Munich crisis, and one of Appleton's first long talks with Bragg concerned the war-time links which would have to be forged between the Cavendish and the staff at Bawdsey, the research station on the east coast whose early radar scanners were covering the Thames Estuary as Chamberlain flew to Munich for his fateful meeting with Adolf Hitler.

Appleton had become involved in the work of air defence later than would at first glance appear to be reasonable. This lay at the root of the strong feelings between himself and Watson-Watt, feelings which were not only to affect his own outlook but to hamper the most efficient use of science during the coming war, and which cannot be ignored in any serious appreciation of Appleton's life and work.

Sir Frederick Brundrett, who from the headquarters of the Admiralty's scientific staff could take an impartial view of affairs, comments: "The only really vivid recollections I have of Appleton during wartime are the appalling difficulties which I got into when caught between the cross-fire of Watson-Watt and Appleton on the subject of who invented radar. Their relations were just about as good as those between Tizard and Lindemann. Appleton certainly would not go near any body with which Watson-Watt was directly concerned." A. P. Rowe, who as Director of the Telecommunications Research Establishment helped to develop the bulk of the war's essential radar devices, comments in much the same vein, while Tizard, deploring, during the war, one aspect of the Watson-Watt–Appleton controversy, wrote that it was "a great pity that the war is so affected by these human considerations, but there it is . . .".

These feelings appear to contrast strongly with Appleton's statement that he sponsored Watson-Watt for Fellowship of the Royal Society in 1941 and his later private comment when writing of the development of radar: "But the biggest effort of all was being made by Watson-Watt, pleading, advocating, hustling, getting in stores, masts, buildings. It was, above all, to his drive and powerful advocacy, that we had radar stations round our coast when war broke out." Similarly, Watson-Watt wrote in *Nature* that "it is morally certain that without the peaceful pursuit of the Board [i.e. the Radio Research Board] and of Appleton and his colleagues in particular, radiolocation would have come too late to have had any decisive influence in the war." The truth is that whatever their private antagonisms both men, when it came to the scientific nub of the matter, adopted towards each other Tizard's honest attitude to Lindemann's courageous work on spinning: "Give the Devil his due."

These antagonisms lay partly in the basic differences between them— Appleton soundly conservative, always anxious to ensure that his actions conformed to the traditions of common sense and good taste; Watson-Watt of a more privateering cut and not over-worried by the perturbations which his actions might cause. Added to this there were their differing views on how the laws of Nature should be exploited; Watson-Watt being, in Appleton's words, "very patent-minded", while Appleton believed that the results of scientific research should be open to all. Nevertheless, the basic disagreements between the two men were really rooted down in the complex genesis of radar, in the long scientific story of lost chances and missed opportunities. They become comprehensible —failing superhuman qualities on both sides, they become almost inevitable—when one considers, chronologically, the significant events which made it possible for Fighter Command to win the Battle of Britain with radar—and, to be fair, for the Luftwaffe to win, in the winter of 1939–40, the first radar contest of the war, the Battle of the Heligoland Bight.

It is undoubtedly true, as Appleton was later to stress, that Watson-Watt was the man who, from early 1935 onwards, was primarily responsible for developing the operational radar system that just tipped the scales in the Battle of Britain. But the record of might-have-beens provides one of the most fascinating lists of modern scientific history and is longer than is often imagined, even by scientists themselves. As far back as 1887 Hertz had shown that radio waves were reflected by metallic objects, and as early as 1904 Holsmeyer was granted patents for an anti-collision device that depended on radio echoes. In the early 1920's Marconi suggested that the same principle might be used by ships at sea, while in the United States Taylor and Young proposed in 1922 that the interruption of radio waves by ships could reveal enemy vessels "irrespective of fog, darkness or smoke-screen". The following year an Austrian was granted a United States patent for what is decribed in official files as "a pulse-modulated type altimeter radar using the radio-wave echo-range principle". And, even before 3 June 1932, when a radio report from the British Post Office discussed the reflection of ultra-short radio waves from aircraft in flight, there had been filed in Britain, early in 1928, a secret provisional patent for what Appleton was later to describe as "a complete patent for radar (both pulse and frequency-modulation)". This was the secret Admiralty patent of Captain Salmond and Mr. Alder of the Admiralty's Signal School, Portsmouth—one of the great missed opportunities and one about which the authorities very naturally were, and have been, extremely sensitive. The principles it invoked included not only the reflection of radio waves, which could be used "for detecting the approach of enemy craft by observation at known positions of the reflection or re-radiation of wireless waves by an approaching ship or aircraft", but also their timing to give distance. For "in some instances the distances between the transmitter and the reflecting object, and the reflecting object and the receiver, may be deduced from the known velocity of the propagation of electromagnetic waves, and the record of the effect or effects observed at the receiver". For some reason best known to the Lords High Commissioner of the Admiralty, the Alder–Salmond patent—which at the least could have reduced the "narrow margin" of the Battle of Britain by an additional 7 years of radar development— "was not proceeded with".

This was the first example in Britain of radar might-have-beens. It was not the last. In 1931 two workers at the Signals Establishment at Woolwich, W. A. S. Butement and P. E. Pollard, devised a system for recording reflected radio pulses, while in the same year the Post Office radio engineers reported the phenomenon which Appleton was to take as a matter of course at the Halley Stewart—a disruption of radio signals when a plane passed nearby. Similar phenomena were reported by the Bell Telephone Company in the United States, while primitive work on the utilisation of radio echoes was soon afterwards being carried out in Germany and Japan.

Most of these precursors of radar—or elementary forms of radar, according to definition—were of a rough-and-ready nature, and although technically ingenious had little practical application. Knowledge of some of them was fairly widespread throughout the scientific world. "It was just the law of nature that aircraft would reflect radio waves, as you would expect them to," Appleton later said when asked his reaction to the Bell Telephone experiment. "There is nothing surprising in that."

Yet these excursions into radio-wave reflection which took place up until the mid-thirties also had two negative characteristics in common. None of them had been devised to meet any urgent operational demand. Moreover, and the vital point as far as Appleton is concerned, none of them, with the exception of the Admiralty patent, utilised the element essential to success in the experiments which had given him the height of the Heaviside Layer: the element which enabled a man on the ground to discover his actual distance from the reflecting material, ionosphere or aircraft, which threw the transmitted radio waves back to him.

This was the situation in the autumn of 1934 when the Secretary of State for Air, Lord Londonderry, at last alarmed by the recent air exercises which showed Britain in general and London in particular to be wide open to air attack from the growing German Air Force, was finally persuaded to take action. This action, urged on by A. P. Rowe through the Air Staff's Scientific Adviser, H. E. Wimperis, was the setting up of what became the famous "Tizard Committee", the Committee for the Scientific Survey of Air Defence, chaired by Sir Henry and comprising, as independent members, the Professor P. M. S. Blackett who had attended some of Appleton's lectures at Cambridge a decade and a half previously, and the distinguished physiologist Professor A. V. Hill. However, before the members of the Committee met for the first time, Wimperis decided to resolve one private and niggling doubt. For years he had been plagued with inventors who wished to demonstrate their own version of a "death-ray", a Flying Dutchman of an idea forever sailing through the seas of the Service world. A decade earlier the Air Ministry had been persuaded to offer £ 1000 for the successful demonstration of such a device and now, at this catalytic moment in the tale of Britain's defences, the story was being revived.

During the previous summer a retired British General had been delayed by a long line of cars while crossing an Alpine pass on the borders of Germany. When he passed the crest he noted, on either side of the pass, two tall radio towers. Jumping to the conclusion that this was confirmation of the "stopped magneto" stories then current, he wrote to the Air Ministry on his return to England suggesting that the Germans were investigating the use of radio waves for some new defence purpose. What is more, he encouraged a number of influential friends to write in similar vein. Neither the General nor his friends were to know that the radio towers had been erected, on Goering's orders, for investigation of television; nor were they to know that the delay was caused merely by a special road barrier, shut at various times so that the radio work would for short periods be unaffected by passing cars.

Wimperis appears to have been equally unaware. Looking at the letters he realised that he could not entirely ignore them; remembering the hocus-pocus of the earlier death-ray claims, he wondered whether the Germans might not be digging in this particular field. He could not entirely rule out the possibility of such a weapon. And he now took the step which was to lead to radar. He asked Watson-Watt, Superintendent of the Radio Research Station at Slough, to visit him at the Air Ministry and to advise him "on the practicability of proposals of the type colloquially called 'death-ray', that is, proposals for producing structural damage or functional derangement in enemy aircraft or their crews".

How Watson-Watt returned to Slough, confirmed that a death-ray was impossible with known techniques, and then asked his assistant, A. F. Wilkins, to discover what power would be required to produce a detectable signal from an aircraft at a specific range, is all well-known. From Wimperis's request there came the famous confirmation to Air Ministry observers at Daventry that aircraft could in fact be detected by reflected radio waves; the seconding of picked workers from Slough to develop what became radar at Bawdsey on the East Coast; and the building, in extreme secrecy, of the first chain of radar warning stations.

The new system operated through the reflection of radio waves from aircraft in much the same way that Appleton's work had utilised the reflection of radio waves from the ionosphere. But while Appleton remained a member of the Radio Research Board, and while his Polar Year data was still being handled by the Slough staff, he himself was for some while kept in ignorance of the top secret defence work being carried out in a field in which he had for years been an acknowledged expert. Some of the Slough staff had grown up under Appleton's guidance and had gained most of their ionospheric expertise from him in the very techniques which were now being developed by Watson-Watt. But if their activities impinged on the early warning work they were warned, under threat of the direst penalties, to keep any hint of this from Appleton. The internal stresses produced a breakdown in at least one member of the staff, whose father wrote that he was "certain that the beginning of [the] illness was when Mr. Watson-Watt told [the person concerned] that secret in connection with the work, and which must not be divulged to you or Mr. Naismith".

Here, more clearly than elsewhere, is an indication of the strains caused by the simple fact that in December 1934 Wimperis had turned to Watson-Watt rather than to Appleton. There were, in fact, very adequate reasons for his choice. Watson-Watt was a radio engineer whereas Appleton was primarily a theoretician — "lacking on the experimental

101

8*

side" as he himself put it. Wimperis must have had, furthermore, a good many qualms about approaching anyone at all about the feasibility of a death-ray, a subject apt to produce broad smiles in academic circles. He could be certain that Watson-Watt, also in government service, would refrain from ridicule; he cannot have been so sure of Appleton, especially in view of the unbridgeable gulf that existed a third of a century ago between the Service authorities on one hand and the academics on the other.

Whatever the exact reason for Wimperis turning to Watson-Watt, the result was that Appleton remained ignorant of the whole radar conception from its beginnings in January 1935 until the summer of 1936. Then, in June, Wimperis suggested that Appleton might be invited to join the Tizard Committee, and on the 17th Tizard wrote to Lord Swinton, chairman of the sub-committee of the CID under whose umbrella the Tizard Committee now worked, formally making the suggestion. Swinton agreed, and on 9 July Appleton was asked to join the Committee.

This was about to be shattered by the Tizard–Lindemann disagreement, and it seems likely that had this internecine dispute not existed Appleton might have been excluded from the developing defence science for even longer. When he accepted on 12 July, a special request was made to him that no publicity should be given to the fact; one reason was that this might suggest that the Committee, whose earlier composition had been announced, was working on a radio defence system. But Tizard had a replacement already "signed up" when, three days later, the Committee disintegrated. It was re-formed only in October. "Lindemann not present, Appleton added to Committee," Tizard noted. "Much better discussion."

Before he made this first attendance as a member of the Tizard Committee Appleton had a brief meeting, at Tizard's request, with Watson-Watt. "Speaking with the latter in the Athenaeum Club, he said it was proposed to detect aircraft by radio," Appleton wrote a decade later. "At once I asked: 'Frequency-change or pulse?' I remember mentioning frequency-change as well as pulse because of its superiority for very short-distance work."

This brief comment is extremely revealing. It underlines that Appleton was not at all surprised at the prospect of detecting aircraft by radio. It highlights Watson-Watt's natural caution — for by this time it was not merely being "proposed" to detect aircraft by radio. Bawdsey was already operating what was to become one of the first five chain stations; the Navy was already investigating how radar could help the Admiralty; individual planes flying in formation had been seen as individuals when they had moved away from one another, while months earlier Watson-Watt had triumphantly reported the height, bearing, and distance of a plane some 75 miles from the coast. It underlines, moreover, the fact that although Appleton was a member of the Radio Research Board, within whose organisation radar had been born, he was being brought into development of the new techniques only after many of the crucial moves had already been taken.

From now onwards he was fully apprised of events at Bawdsey. From Cambridge, little more than 50 miles away, he made regular visits to the station, finding the workers there apt to try out their ideas on him. "They were such a fertile crowd that they gave one no room for suggestions," he commented. He did, however, put forward one idea made when there was difficulty in providing British aircraft with some means of differentiating themselves from other planes picked up on the radar screens. Watson-Watt had suggested the use of a wire dipole, but this had to be accommodated outside the aircraft, which was a disadvantage. Appleton suggested that, instead, a "squegger" circuit be arranged so that the device would only operate when triggered off by the pulse from the radar stations. "The advantage I saw in this," he later wrote, "was that the 'squegg' from the oscillator in the aircraft could be made at a slightly different radio-frequency from the prompting impulses. In this way, by simple tuning, one could, on the cathode-ray screen, separate friends from foes."

It is quite clear that from now onwards both Wimperis and Tizard — neither of whom were radio men — leaned heavily on Appleton for their appreciations of how well the radar work was being pushed on under Watson-Watt. Thus Wimperis wrote revealing to Tizard in September 1936 — before Appleton had in fact attended any meetings of the Tizard Committee — saying: "I think it would be a useful thing if one of us, preferably you, had a talk as soon as possible with Appleton, who, as a result of his periodical visits, must have made up his mind on the technical merits of the work being carried out." Two months later Appleton wrote to Tizard, equally revealingly, a letter whose tone is well summed up by its first two sentences: "You may be sure that if I knew of anything behind the scenes you would be informed. I don't think there is anything amiss except that Watson-Watt is not building up an enormous organisation as rapidly as he desires." Four years later Watson-Watt's scientific empire building, irritating though it may have appeared to Appleton, more than proved its worth.

By the autumn of 1937 Appleton was thus not only carrying out the duties of the Jacksonian Professor, and handling the bulk of the administrative work at the Cavendish, but was also increasingly involved in the spreading defence affairs of the Tizard Committee. As the link-man with the Cavendish he was directly involved with plans for the laboratory if war should start. These plans, like much else stemming from government irresolution, were vague in the extreme. This is made clear in a letter which Appleton wrote to Tizard on 27 September 1938, two days before Chamberlain signed the Munich Agreement. "I had a talk with Bragg on Saturday, during which we made up a list of key Cavendish people," this went. "I gather from what Cockcroft has told me that this list has already been made use of.

"On thinking over the question of the Bawdsey evacuation, I have felt that the Cavendish group and their mechanical staff would, if a selection were made, make an excellent nucleus for research on the problem you have in mind, or on other matters. Time could also be saved by our commandeering a good deal of Cavendish apparatus. I am therefore making out a list of people and apparatus in case you want me to move them bodily to some place. Could you let me know what you think about this? I do not know what plans you have to suggest for myself, but if need be I could run this group, since they are all people who are well known to me.

"Could you let me know whether it is your view that such a group should work at the new site of the Bawdsey personnel or whether you consider they might operate separately at Cambridge or elsewhere?

"I have been looking into the Cavendish needs, and think that they can best be catered for by the elder men, so that our *best* people will be available.

"If you would like me to come to Town to see you, please send me a wire, and I will catch the first train. There are many other points we might discuss concerning the recruitment of scientific people."

It is clear from this that at the end of September 1938 Appleton had no certainty about what his role would be in the war that many thought likely and that many were to see as inevitable after the Munich capitulation. He had, however, already been earmarked, according to a "Note on the Organisation of the Technical Work at the Air Ministry in the Event of War", apparently prepared by Tizard this same month. "The people I have in mind are as follows," this began. "a) Professor E. V. Appleton. He has really already been selected and it is clear that he will be wanted for radio work...."

These plans were to be altered and they were to be altered with quite surprising speed. On 21 October Bragg was writing to Sir Frank Smith, Secretary of the Department of Scientific and Industrial Research, about the use of scientists in the war effort. In November Tizard was writing to Smith about the same subject. Yet before the end of the month Appleton had agreed to take up, for a 5-year period, the secretaryship which was now being vacated by Smith. It is not quite clear to whom the credit for the appointment should go; however, in a stray note written years later, Appleton himself implies that this might have been the elder Bragg, in 1938 Director of the Faraday Laboratory at the Royal Institution, President of the Royal Society, and the man who had doggedly been trying to convince the Government that if war broke out science and scientists would have a part to play in it.

The move appears to have been unpremeditated; but it was to be unexpectedly successful.

CHAPTER 7

1939–1945: THE WAR: RUNNING THE DSIR

IN THE autumn of 1938 the Secretary of the Department of Scientific and Industrial Research, Sir Frank Smith, was approaching the age at which retirement might be likely. To even the most optimistic it seemed that war was only just over the horizon; it would obviously be preferable if the head of such a department throughout the coming conflict were able to learn the administrative ropes during the few months of peace that remained; and so, in October, Sir Frank decided to retire.

There were few obvious candidates for what was likely to become an increasingly demanding post, however reluctant the authorities might be to admit that science was already obtruding deeply into what they still considered to be the gentlemanly arts of war. The first Secretary, Sir Frank Heath, had been a man of many parts; professor of English, government administrator, and an amateur scientist who had designed the British "tin-hat" in the shape of the Japanese samurai helmet. His successor, Sir Henry Tizard, had forged strong links between Government and industry during his work on flight testing before he came to the Department in 1923. Tizard's successor, the Sir Frank Smith who was now retiring, had matured in the government atmosphere of the National Physical Laboratory before becoming the first head of the Admiralty's Scientific Research Service. By comparison, Appleton had concentrated on radio and the more esoteric field of the ionosphere, even though his knowledge of physics was wide; his links with industry were mainly with the radio manufacturers and even these, while greater than those of most contemporary academics, were hardly of a major character. If his knowledge of current defence work through membership of the Tizard Committee was put in the balance this would have tended to suggest a war-time post in one of the Services—although the most obvious, the Air Ministry, might have been ruled out by the figure of Watson-Watt, already occupying the high ground.

However, this injection of the Jacksonian Professor into the world of Department politics was a success. It was to be so because there was another side to the Appleton coin. There was his brisk handling of administrative affairs which had made a deep impression in the Cavendish after Rutherford's death. To this ability, which had only recently been revealed, Appleton added an impartiality in judgement that had an almost High Court quality; he was by nature non-partisan, and some able civil servant may well have divined how useful this quality would be in the internecine struggles which the stresses of war might bring. In addition, Appleton exhibited another valuable quality. He kept his head. He did not worry, and in the worst crises he had a habit of saying: "Let's live a day at a time." Perhaps it was his Yorkshire upbringing; perhaps it was simply character. But it seemed unlikely that he would crack under the strain. Together with the high scientific regard in which he was held, these qualities combined to make his choice far less of a gamble than it looked in some quarters.

There remains the question of Appleton's own acceptance of the post. It seems that he had no particular liking for administrative work, even though so able at it. He rarely evinced any particular attraction to the Civil Service. And his life-long feeling for science as a probing of the world's natural mysteries hardly fitted him for the application of science to industry which was the Department's normal work. Yet his patriotism, always of the simple, uncritical kind, could easily be called upon. It was clear that throughout a war any ionospheric work at Cambridge would be severely limited. Moreover, as the Secretary of the DSIR he would have a link with Slough, with the Radio Research Station whose ionospheric work would, perhaps ironically, come directly within his chain of command. These were all significant points, and in February Appleton moved to London with his family, no doubt believing with the current optimism of the time that his five-year agreement would carry him through and beyond any war that was likely to start within the next few months.

The Department to which Appleton now came as head had been set up early in the First World War. Until 1914, Britain had been forced to import from Germany the 30,000 tons of potash she needed annually; was dependent on the enemy for the tungsten needed by steelmakers; produced barely a tenth of the dyestuffs she required; imported from Germany zinc smelted from ore produced in the Empire; and had been equipping a considerable part of her Army's artillery with gun-sights made by Goertz of Berlin. The DSIR had been set up to help rectify this unhappy state of affairs; its aim not to give direct aid to the war effort but to help create a more scientific basis for British industry and one which would make the country more self-sufficient. This aim was developed and expanded throughout the inter-war years with the setting-up of government research stations dealing with roads, fuel, and food — as well as with radio and many other matters; in addition, the Department sponsored research associations which were financially supported by both industry and the Government.

During the 1930's there had been a slight but subtle change of emphasis. The Department still operated under the umbrella of the Lord President of the Council, who was in turn advised by an advisory council composed of men from industry and from science. But an increasing amount of its work was of use, even if indirectly, to the Armed Forces, and one writer has gone so far as to claim that by 1937 more than a third of the Department's money could "be credited to war and is fairly closely connected with possible war uses". It was certainly clear by early 1939 that the process would have to be taken a stage further as soon as war broke out, and preparations for this were already beginning when Appleton took up his new post.

For a short while he continued to live in Cambridge, travelling up to stay in London throughout the week and winding up his Jacksonian and Johnian duties at the weekend. Then, early in the spring, he moved to London, taking a flat on Putney Hill from which he could easily travel each day to the departmental headquarters in Old Queen Street, the first of a series of moves which were to uproot the family during the next few years.

He was quickly submerged in a major problem—that of the Department's scientific manpower and the best method of deploying it when war broke out. The Royal Society had already forced a reluctant Government to take the measures which were to result in the setting-up of what became the Central Register. However, Appleton quickly realised that this would not be enough. It was important that teams of men, working together on research problems, should not be broken up unless there was an overwhelming reason for doing this. "It was realised," he later wrote, "that there would be a need for maintaining research groups as units, and the Department instituted a register of the various scientific research groups, both industrial and university, in the country. . . . Since it was known that it would be necessary greatly to expand the Service research establishment staffs, it was decided at the outset to maintain the industrial units as teams, at least in the initial stages of the war, but it was also decided that the members of the university teams should be made available as individuals to augment the service establishments."

This policy of directing the academic scientists into positions where they could utilise their existing skills in new conditions was to prove one of the outstanding successes of the war. Distinguished mathematicians left astronomy to study the flight of shells. Biologists successfully handled the problems of radar and operational research, while one geneticist was almost to double the available flying time of Coastal Command by a scientific reorganisation of maintenance schedules. However, the corollary to this was that the teams already working on relevant problems in industry, or in the research stations of DSIR, should not be broken up. Appleton maintained that a team working on one problem in the National Physical Laboratory was of far more use to the war effort if its members were not dispersed to Service research establishments for work on similar problems there. "In the main, his views prevailed," says one of those working with him at the time, "though not without much argument and difficulty. No doubt each side saw the other as prejudiced, Appleton appearing to some as unreasonably resisting their just claims to man-power, and being too concerned not to see his own domain depopulated; and Appleton believing that others were too ready to see the advantages of having men immediately at hand, albeit often with appallingly inadequate facilities, and too prone to underestimate the disadvantages of leaving DSIR's material facilities under-manned, not to mention the human problems and the problems of living accommodation which transfers involved and which ought not to be created in unnecessary degree."

These plans for the deployment of the staff were complete by September 1939 when, on the outbreak of war, the headquarters was evacuated to the Department's Chemical Research Laboratory, itself situated in the grounds of the National Physical Laboratory at Teddington. And it was from here that Appleton turned his efforts to the multiple duties which were to absorb him throughout the war years.

These duties were of great variety, and they spread out across a considerable sector of the country's war-time scientific effort – both civilian and Service. If they were only infrequently at the highest level – and Appleton scarcely operated within the inner Churchillian councils where the most important decisions were made – the manner in which they were carried out did help to lower the temperature in over-heated situations, to resolve the almost unresolvable arguments that often occurred, and to decrease the internal friction which at times threatened to bring the country's scientific effort to a standstill. A minor but typical example was provided when Air Marshal Harris, Commander-in-Chief, Bomber Command, stoutly declared that an independent meteorological service was essential to his squadrons and the Meteorological Office as stoutly declared the reverse. Appleton was brought in to chair the committee set up to pronounce on the argument – and did so in a manner which placated both parties, even if it did not satisfy them.

An indication of how he was able to do so is given by Sir Philip Morris, Director-General of Army Education in the latter part of the war, whose path crossed Appleton's more than once. "I remember him as a man who was so much bigger than his job that his personal relations remained easy," he says. "He did not have to put up smoke screens or otherwise cover up. Certainly he inspired me with confidence in him – and I should think this was generally true."

The secretaryship of the DSIR of course provided the major, and the continuing, bulk of work, since Appleton sat at the head of a chain of command which included the directors not only of the National Physical Laboratory, but of the Geological Survey, and of organisations dealing with food investigation, and research into building, forest products, fuel, pest infestation, radio, roads, and water pollution. Most of these groups had their own advisory committees as well as their directors who controlled the research "on the ground", and to this extent the headquarters organisation could be considered in a scientific as distinct from an administrative and general management sense, as a "post office" through which either the Government or industry passed its demands. On to Appleton, the only man who could easily assess resources available, there thus fell the burden of recommending whether any specific project to aid the war could, or should, be handled by one of his stations.

During the preceding two decades, most of these stations had built up an impressive list of experimental and test facilities, most of which now came under demand from the Services. Thus the massive cold chamber which had been built at the Ditton Research Station to test the reactions of fruit under refrigeration was used to discover how barrage balloons might behave in the cold of the higher atmosphere. The Fuel Research Station was conscripted to test the potentialities of petroleum warfare and the possibilities of "setting the sea on fire" when the invasion of Britain appeared to be imminent. The National Physical Laboratory was involved in a score of ways, its workers devising ingenious methods of defusing unexploded bombs, and its ship tank being used to develop landing craft, the Mulberry Harbours and, perhaps most famous of all, Barnes Wallis's bouncing bombs which destroyed the Mohne Dam. Both the Road Research Station and the Building Research Station, with their expert knowledge of concrete structures, were brought into the work that preceded the attack on the dams. The Forest Products Research Station helped aircraft-makers use plywood and adhesives in planes. The Fuel Research Station produced fuel for flame-throwers—and by suggesting how ships' boiler-doors could be modified to prevent smoke-emission saved the lives of many thousand merchant seamen, as did the Water Pollution Research Laboratory's chemical means of converting sea-water into drinking water.

Demands for all such facilities were, in effect, shuttled through the narrow doorway of Appleton's office, and it would have been excusable for such an office to show, during the stresses of wartime, a slight touch of pandemonium. This was usually avoided; one reason was Appleton's unflusterable Yorkshire calm. He never gave the appearance of being rushed or panicked; he would rarely say: "I've decided in my bath this morning"—but rather: "I've decided during the last day or so." He was a great non-worrier, so organising both himself and his work that he rarely gave an indication of the volume he was handling—a volume to which the DSIR itself contributed only a part.

A typical day at the office—where he arrived for work one Christmas morning on the grounds that everyone else had to be there and he saw no reason for his own exemption—would start with the routine of dealing with urgent post, reading the latest DSIR files, and signing the authorisations for urgent work. He would then dictate letters or minutes prepared at home, and by mid-morning would normally be seeing the first of his constant stream of visitors.

At times he would interview them in his car, the car which was frequently driven by W. R. Piggott, his ionospheric colleague who had gone with him from King's College to Cambridge. With Appleton's departure from Cambridge, Piggott had at first moved to Slough. Then, on the outbreak of war, Appleton had asked that he should be seconded to DSIR headquarters; and from then onwards Piggott was to occupy an unusual position at Appleton's right hand, helping him deal with the ionospheric work that came his way, advising him on a multitude of curious tasks, and frequently acting as his private chauffeur.

One afternoon a week Appleton reserved for special consultation with Piggott. Together they dealt with the "mad ideas" which multiplied during the early years of the war, and which included a project for attaching magnets to fish to deal with magnetic mines—a suggestion from no less a man than Professor J. B. S. Haldane—and the freezing of clouds. The proposals could be ignored only at peril—after all, it had been a final investigation of the "death-ray" which had produced radar. Thus it was that Appleton was involved in one particularly maddening diversion. It came late in 1940 and at the instigation of the Prime Minister himself.

Churchill had been written to by the editor of the *Manchester Guardian*, William Crozier, who reported that an inventor in Lancashire had devised an apparatus claimed to be "capable of televising large fields of observation, whether on land, on sea, or in the air, and producing the television pictures on screens at a considerable number of miles from the objects televised". The supporting details tended to increase suspicion of what was already a suspicious claim. However, the claim came when airborne radar was still beset with teething troubles, and when no protection against the night bomber seemed likely in the foreseeable future. Churchill passed on the letter to the Lord President of the Council, Neville Chamberlain, under whose umbrella the DSIR operated, with instructions that the claim should be investigated. Chamberlain passed the letter to Appleton and in due course Appleton had to investigate personally.

The head of the DSIR therefore found himself, accompanied by Dr. Smith-Rose, then head of the Radio Division of the National Physical Laboratory, inspecting what appeared to be a series of electric light bulbs in a small Lancashire town. With their aid, it was claimed, a picture could be seen of the summit of Snowdon, more than 60 miles away across Liverpool Bay; but, as in the case of the recurrent death-ray, something always happened to prevent translation of the miracle from promise to fact. However, Appleton and Smith-Rose felt obliged to waste much time and energy before returning south to report that there appeared nothing whatsoever to support the claims. The inventor, like many others, refused to take "no" for an answer and his appeals for a further hearing crop up intermittently throughout the war years—sometimes with surprising supporters.

Appleton did not float above such problems solely on account of his wide technical knowledge or his mastery of the Civil Service machine, whose devices he had quickly mastered but with which he appears to have had no particular sympathy. Indeed, he was later fond of explaining how after leaving the DSIR he had come upon a literary paper entitled "Various aspects of the negative", and of then commenting: "For the moment, as an ex-Civil Servant, I thought it must be a Treasury document!" His strength lay elsewhere, in his ability to arouse the help and loyalty of his staff, a purely human ability which had nothing to do with science or business efficiency but was possibly the most important key to Appleton's character. He disliked hurting people, a factor which tended to limit his efficiency in the brutal world of higher politics; yet a concern for the men and women who worked with him helped to carry the Department through the war and out into the peace with greater strength than before. His brief notes to those away ill— "get better quickly; we're getting on disappointingly well without you"—invariably had a human touch. Minor honour or local success achieved by a junior member of the staff in stations under his control would frequently bring a brief note of congratulation from the Secretary, often to the surprise of the recipient. In his early days at headquarters the door of an office would sometimes open and in he would come. "My name's Appleton," he would say before sitting down and asking how things were going. His interest was easily aroused, and his stay was frequently lengthened.

These personal characteristics were noted at all levels. "Appleton always gave careful consideration to the views of the staff," one permanent civil servant noted after his death. "Two examples come to mind. First his meeting with staff representatives to consider the organisation of the DSIR for war service, and secondly the careful and detailed personal consideration he gave to appeals against assimilation to the new salary scales and grades introduced in 1945. The assimilation affected every member of the DSIR scientific staff. In such a large-scale operation it was inevitable that many individuals were not satisfied with their assimilation. The Secretary personally devoted two and a half days to hearing appeals put forward by the Institution and as a result many members had their position improved. At the end of the hearings Appleton devoted a further half day to discussing Institution policy regarding the Scientific Civil Service with the General Secretary, Leslie Herbert, and other Institution representatives."

Appleton, his wife, and his younger daughter Rosalind—his elder daughter Margery having already married the Rev. William Lamont, a Church of England minister who had joined the Royal Navy in 1941, had subsequently been commissioned, and later became a naval chaplain —moved after their Putney home had been damaged in the blitz, and on 15 September 1940, he noted in his diary: "Came to Teddington to stay at Clarence Hotel." This was a smallish establishment lying almost up against the walls of Bushy Park in which the National Physical Laboratory stands. Here the Appletons settled in comfortably. "It is much further from London and the bombing is not so intensive here," he wrote reassuringly to his parents and sister in Bradford. "We've now got some big deck-chairs which are just like beds and we settle down with pillows and rugs for the night in the shelter under the hotel. We've been given a special place near the beer barrels where we are cut off from the rest of the other shelterers. We are highly favoured. The place is so strong with beams (it has been specially strengthened by the town council) that if the whole place came down on top of it we should be alright. A number of the people in the hotel sleep in their rooms but we think it only prudent to use the shelter."

Prudence was perhaps justified since the nearby National Physical Laboratory was hit more than once. During one raid a delayed action bomb dropped on the experimental ship-testing tank and was duly removed by a bomb disposal company of the Royal Engineers. Appleton reacted in his usual way. "I remember," he noted years later, "giving a complimentary supper to the officers and men after the bomb had been raised."

With the headquarters of the DSIR evacuated to the nearby Chemical Research Laboratory, the Clarence Hotel was convenient, but after a while the Appletons moved back to their flat in Putney until, in 1942, the turn of events took them back to Teddington. For in 1942 Sir Charles Darwin, Director of the National Physical Laboratory, was seconded to the British Mission in Washington. Appleton became, in effect, Acting Director of the NPL as well as Secretary of the DSIR—yet another item added to his by this time multitudinous posts. And he and his family now moved into the Director's apartments of Bushy House, formerly the residence of the Ranger, who had occupied it when the Court was at Hampton Court Palace. An exquisite building looking out on the 1000-acre park with its deer and its famous avenue of chestnuts enclosed in a fourfold avenue of limes, Bushy House had had a long line of illustrious occupants and had finally been given by Queen Victoria in the closing years of her reign as the headquarters of the newly founded NPL.

As always, Appleton "did his homework" and read up the history of the beautiful building that had been the Director's residence for almost half a century. What he learned intrigued him, as he remembered years later. "It was there," he said, speaking to the Institution of Electrical Engineers, "that William IV, before he married and settled down, lived with an actress for nine years and produced nine little Fitz-Clarences. Do you know what we decided to use the building for? The maintenance of the national standards—the national standards of frequency, inductance and capacity."

In 1941 Appleton was made a Knight Commander of the Bath, the award that customarily went with the secretaryship of the DSIR. He was delighted, and wrote proudly and uninhibitedly in describing the ceremony to "Dear All"—his mother, father, and sister Dorothy. "The Knighthoods came early so I had not long to wait before I had to kneel before his Majesty who touched both shoulders with his sword," he wrote. "He then put round my neck a decoration and a star on my left breast. He then shook hands, I bowed, and it was all over!

"So now you have to address letters, if you are writing to me alone, Sir Edward Appleton, KCB, FRS *or* if you are writing to us both, Sir Edward and Lady Appleton.

"We then came back to the flat in a taxi bringing with me the lovely decorations in a nice case with which I was presented. I then got out of my tall hat, morning coat, etc. and we went out into Putney High Street to lunch. Rosalind was allowed to have just what she liked as it was a special occasion, so she chose Tomato juice cocktail, fish and chips, ice cream and ginger beer!!! Jessie had turkey etc.

"If there had not been fear of air raids we should, of course, have gone into London itself but Jessie was cautious. Actually, we had an air raid while we were in the Palace!

"After the Knighthood came quite a lot of soldiers, civil defence workers and nurses. One air officer got DSO, DFC and bar all at once. I think he ought to have been first before all the civilians!..."

It is probably true, even though curious, that Appleton's piloting of the DSIR through the war, a solid achievement of which he had every reason to be justly proud, was overshadowed in importance not only by his work on a number of war-time committees but also by his war-time work in preparing the Department for the peace. It is true that he was interested in the ionosphere first of all, but after that he was interested in the

needs of the ordinary citizen; the great struggles for command of the air
or of the seas had only a passing interest for him, and it was natural that,
in mid-war, he should become personally committed to the plans for
peace-time reconstruction which the Government was already courage-
ously making.

Appleton had from the first looked upon the DSIR as a "do" rather
than a "don't" department. He knew that a first priority of the peace
would be the reconstruction of roads and of houses, the revival of industry, and the development for civilian use of the multiple devices,
techniques, and materials which had been produced under the stress of
war-time necessity. He believed that science in general and the DSIR in
particular had a vital part to play in this reconstruction, and he threw himself with great energy into the work of the Post-war Developments Committee which was set up in 1943. It was no doubt this enthusiasm which
led to the story, still believed in many quarters although probably apocryphal, that in briefing Lord Woolton – Lord President of the Council for two
months in the summer of 1945 – Appleton included, in brackets, the comment "this is not a very plausible argument but it will be good enough to
satisfy their Lordships", a comment which, it is alleged, Woolton was
so unfortunate as to read with his statement.

Appleton was thus at the heart of the very ambitious plans for expansion of the DSIR which were prepared during the final months of the war.
Given the increased awareness of science which the war brought about,
such an expansion was inevitable; yet it seems certain that this expansion
would have been pushed through less successfully, with more residual ill-
will from those who objected to science having a larger cut of the national
cake, had it not been for Appleton's conciliatory hand on the tiller as the
operation was piloted through government channels.

Two beliefs stand out from what he wrote and said on the subject
during the significant periods. One was the need to reduce the distinction
between pure and applied science; the other was the urgent necessity for
industry to apply scientific principles to its practice and management –
both requirements that have a curiously current ring about them despite
their emphasis by Appleton a quarter of a century ago. Both points were
made clear as early as 1942 when on 1 July Appleton's Personal Assistant,

Christopher Joliffe, sent to the War Cabinet Offices a brief for the debate on the post-war reorganisation of science to be held at Westminster some days later.

"First and most important of all," this went, "we must have the best scientific brains of the country devoting their efforts to research for the benefit of industry and the community generally. The old stigma attaching to 'applied' as opposed to 'pure' research must be forgotten. But that does not mean that scientists working in industrial laboratories should spend all their energies only in solving day-to-day problems of the factory. A study of the fundamental scientific principles is often the quickest and most effective way of solving what seems to be a purely practical problem. What is needed is the brains of the most able scientists, working in an atmosphere of freedom in which they can study practical problems in collaboration with the men on the job, tackling them in their own way and, moreover, given the freedom to mix with their more academic colleagues in Universities in study and discussion...

"Again and again, fundamental discoveries in science made in this country have been first applied to practical ends by foreign competitors. This can never be cured as long as industry regards research as an expensive extra to be dispensed with in times of economic stringency. The scientific spirit must be part of the industrial outlook. This will only come about when part of the training for industry is a sound technological education."

These barriers between "pure" and "applied" science, between science and industry, were only some of those which tended to keep scientists in water-tight compartments. There were others, including the barrier between science and the Services, that had in fact been considerably reduced during the war, a reduction in which Appleton had played an honourable part.

"I used to keep saying that we should 'hunt in couples', meaning that the partnership between the operational man and the scientists should be a close one," he wrote after the war. "As you say, 'the user does not know what it is reasonable to ask for and the provider may not know what needs providing'. However, a close partnership, with no secrets withheld from the scientist, often works wonders in this connection. Very often I found it was a good thing for the scientist to keep making suggestions, trying of course to be relevant, for this prompted the user to ask for something he'd not previously thought possible." This was particularly relevant to Operational Research, mainly because "the whole subject of war-like operations had been kept so secret previously. No-one but a Serviceman could possibly have anything to contribute to its development. Certain doctrines had been formulated and were invested with such authority that it was disloyal and heretical to question them. All the scientist did, when at last he was allowed within the mystic circle, was to question everything that was being done; and if he could get enough data, to try to test all accepted doctrines in numerical fashion."

It was reasonable enough that such comments should come from Appleton. For few scientists had been more variously occupied with the task of bridging the gap between the scientist in his research laboratory and the pilot in the air or the destroyer captain on anti-submarine patrol.

Cherwell and Tizard operated on a different level, while men such as Lockspeiser in the Ministry of Aircraft Production and Blackett at the Admiralty could look back on an intimate years-long acquaintance with defence problems. Appleton's influence was of a different sort, produced mainly by his wartime contacts, new but numerous, at a multitude of points along the frontiers where science met industry and the Services.

CHAPTER 8

1939–1945: THE WAR: SCIENCE AND THE SERVICES

APPLETON'S impact on the war of 1939–45 has been appreciated less than it deserves. One reason lies in his own inclination to avoid the jungle warfare which frequently engages those with the ambition that drives to high command in war — Service or civilian; and it was thus typical that he should write to Tizard that he did not "want to get involved in the R.D.F. circus of 'political' self-seekers". This objective attitude, qualified only by his feelings towards Watson-Watt, tended to keep him from both the inner cabals where the really important decisions of the scientific war were made, and from the limelight that played upon the centre of the circus ring. This attitude was, furthermore, reinforced by an over-deep respect for the conventional approach during a period when privateering was the order of the day. Thus his contributions were of the non-flashy sort, typified by the quiet but essential word behind the scenes, the balanced verdict when tempers were running short and — possibly most important of all — the judgement which he was capable of bringing to bear on the purely scientific problem. While these factors tended to emphasise Appleton's work within the DSIR, the haphazard manner in which the facts of the scientific war have trickled out during the last quarter of a century have tended to emphasise, purely fortuitously, some aspects of what he did and to gloss over others more worthy of note. Thus he is possibly best known for his "over-lordship", as Secretary of the DSIR, of the Tube Alloys project, Britain's atomic bomb organisation, even though his department acted virtually as a post-box through which instructions were passed to the Tube Alloys workers under Sir Wallace Akers; while his more pervasive if less obvious influence on events through membership of a score of committees has been less noted.

Appleton's introduction to current defence problems had, of course, come with his membership of the Tizard Committee in 1936. Thenceforward he had become increasingly concerned with the experiments supported by the Committee. He had visited Bawdsey frequently, had been given the use of Royal Air Force aircraft to help with radio-sonde experiments carried out from Cambridge early in 1938, and after the re-constitution of the Tizard Committee on the outbreak of war — when it was merged with a later committee on Aerial Offence — had been drawn into work which he could personally supervise from the DSIR.

"I have to remind you of the recommendation of the new Committee for the Scientific Survey of Air Warfare at the Meeting at Oxford on September 27th," wrote the Committee's Secretary on 5 October 1939, "recommending that you and Dr. Darwin should consider, in consultation with DSR Admiralty, the possibility of evolving methods for the location of submerged submarines from aircraft; and that you be empowered to call in Professor A. O. Rankin and any other scientists who in your view may be of assistance in this investigation.

"Also you will remember that you agreed to discuss with Mr. Watson-Watt the possibilities of the suggestion you made for equipping warships with RDF receiving apparatus so that the presence of aircraft flying in their vicinity would be revealed, using the transmissions from the Coastal Chain Stations...."

Shortly afterwards it was recommended that he should continue with his "experimental work in an endeavour to locate unknown radio stations which use pulse transmissions". And the records reinforce the fact that during the 9 months of "the phoney war" Appleton's left hand was constantly occupied with helping the reformed Tizard Committee while his right hand was dealing with the multiple problems of the DSIR.

It was thus inevitable that he should feel implicated when, in the summer of 1940, with Churchill hoisted into Downing Street and Cherwell beside him, Tizard should be squeezed into resignation and his committee eliminated. Appleton's Olympian detachment allowed him to remain on good terms with both Tizard and Cherwell, even though he was well aware of the latter's weaknesses. "Take it to Cherwell," was his advice when a colleague at the DSIR came to him with a project for which he wanted support, "and tell him it's just been turned down by Tizard." And, just as revealingly of himself as of Cherwell, he noted in one of his small books of random jottings: "Lindemann: I say of him that if you work alone you make mistakes. You need the checking of your colleagues to be sure."

When Tizard was finally forced out in June 1940, Appleton wrote consolingly, but with a concluding hope that showed his ignorance of what had been going on. "My dear Tizard," went his letter, "Your resignation is a major tragedy. I make out that the present high efficiency of our air offence and defence has followed largely from your personal influence (via ARC and DSSAW) which, among other things, has brought about a fruitful and easy collaboration between Air Staff representatives and scientists. I do not see these relations being continued now without you. We've had every reason to call it the Tizard Committee and, as I see it, if the 'Tizard' goes the 'Committee' goes too. Is there no way of retrieving the situation?"

The demise of Tizard's Committee for the Scientific Survey of Air Warfare reduced by one the number of groups whose meetings Appleton had to attend and which provided him with a constant flow of work outside the DSIR. There remained a wide assortment, ranging from the Scientific Advisory Committee to the Cabinet, set up in October 1940, to the cumbersome Advisory Council on Scientific Research and Technical Development of the Ministry of Supply; there remained the Camouflage Committee, the Substitutes Committees, and the Civil Defence Research Committee which he had chaired since it was set up at the beginning of the war. He was a member of Lord Hankey's Committee which helped to allocate the available technicians, and of numerous other groups which carried on throughout the whole six years of war. In addition, he served on various *ad hoc* groups, such as the Guy Committee set up in May 1942 to investigate armament development, while in the spring of the following year he carried out, on the Prime Minister's direction, a special investigation into the resources devoted to research in various government departments.

All this consumed time and energy, so that many of Appleton's wartime days began with an hour or so at headquarters, continued with a shuttling back and forth between meetings in various parts of London, and ended with an informal session in the Athenaeum. So much of his continuing business was conducted there that he laid down his own rule: "Decisions of the Advisory Council of the DSIR to count only if they are taken at headquarters: those at the Athenaeum not to be included."

Much of this work provided the background detail to the major themes, those of Tube Alloys, of the Cabinet's Scientific Advisory Council, of radar, and ionospheric work. The Tube Alloys work on nuclear fission was formally brought under the DSIR in the early autumn of 1941, but Appleton's connection with the subject went back almost exactly two years, to 17 August 1939 when the Tizard Committee, of which he was then a member, asked the Air Ministry to supply a ton of uranium oxide to Professors Moon and Oliphant in Birmingham University. This would supplement work which Appleton's old colleague, G. P. Thomson, was doing in London. There had been an earlier British move on the matter when in the spring of 1939 General Ismay, Secretary of the Committee of Imperial Defence, had instructed Tizard to carry out a personal and extremely secret survey of nuclear possibilities, but it is not certain that Appleton was informed of this. Certainly it seems likely that in the rush of other duties he overlooked the Tizard Committee's later action; for when, in October 1939, he was asked by Lord Hankey whether he had any information on the subject of nuclear weapons, he wrote inquiringly to Chadwick. Professor Chadwick, another former colleague of the Cavendish and by this time the country's leading nuclear physicist, replied cautiously, promised to consider the subject of a weapon, and said that he would write again.

Chadwick's second letter, which reached Appleton at the DSIR early in December 1939, said that he had been investigating two types of fission. "The conclusions I have reached are these," he went on. "It seems likely that both types of fission—the one due to thermal neutrons, the second to fast neutrons – could be developed to an explosive process under appropriate conditions. . . . I think it would be desirable to get some information on the mechanism and if I can get enough uranium oxide I will do so. I have here a Polish research man [Professor Rotblat] who has some experience in this work and who is very able and very quick."

Appleton passed Chadwick's information to both Tizard and the War Cabinet whose Secretariat now suggested that Tizard might link up the work that was being carried on; fearing, in the words of the official atomic energy history, "that in the body of scientists the right hand did not know what the left hand was doing". The fear was well justified. Within a few months the famous Maud Committee had been set up by Tizard under G. P. Thomson to prepare what was in some ways a blue-print for an atomic bomb; yet even a year later, in February 1941, Appleton had been told very little about its activities, while Hankey, the chairman of the Cabinet's Scientific Advisory Committee set up a few months earlier, "did not", in the words of the official history, "even know of its existence".

Thus there was a fair back-log of crossed lines when the Maud Committee reported in the summer of 1941 that a nuclear weapon was probably feasible. They had been increased before Appleton was informed, some months later, that his Department had been selected as the cover under which "Tube Alloys", Britain's first practical work on a nuclear weapon, would soon be operating. His first reaction was a sober scientific one – to insist that the Geological Survey, a body under the DSIR, should immediately start a survey of the Empire's uranium resources. Significantly, while the Defence Services Panel of the Cabinet's Scientific Advisory Committee, with Appleton a member, decided only on 25 September to recommend that work on the bomb should be formally begun, the vital decision had been taken and the machinery started 2 months earlier when Churchill had acted personally on Cherwell's recommendation and nominated Sir John Anderson, the new Lord President of the Council, as the Cabinet Minister responsible.

With the formal start of Tube Alloys, Appleton found himself, as in more than one subsequent chapter of the nuclear story, forced to cope with the problems of an unwanted baby suddenly thrust into his arms. In the words of the official history: "The new Directorate [of Tube Alloys] was formed without any consultation with the scientists who had started the project and was imposed dictatorially upon them." Upon Appleton, therefore, there now fell the task of explaining the position. Professor Oliphant, one of the first men involved in the work, felt so strongly that he protested: "I can quite understand," he wrote to Appleton, "why it may be desirable for DSIR to take control of the Maud work rather than leave it with MAP [Ministry of Aircraft Production]. On the other hand I can see no reason whatever why the people put in charge of this work should be commercial representatives completely ignorant of the essential nuclear physics upon which the whole thing is based. . . . "Appleton smoothed the feelings, very justifiably ruffled, as best he could.

There was still, however, the question of the "commercial representatives completely ignorant of the nuclear physics upon which the whole thing is based". Here it is quite clear where Appleton's sympathies lay. He had strong views about the commercial exploitation of the laws of nature; and the SAC Panel which had considered the Maud Committee's report had decided at its very first meeting that it could not approve a Ministry of Aircraft Production proposal to turn over the civilian potentialities of nuclear energy to Imperial Chemical Industries—even though the company had played an important part in the exploratory work. Now, however, Appleton found that the man who was to run the organisation put under the umbrella of his own department was Wallace, later Sir Wallace Akers, Research Director of ICI; his second-in-command was to be Akers's own deputy, Michael, later Sir Michael Perrin. "This verges on the Gilbertian," wrote one senior official. "The Government decide to turn down ICI's request to be allowed to run the developments and then ask ICI to let them have the chief protagonist of the ICI request to manage the matter for the Government." However, Appleton's task was not to reason why; during the years that followed he dutifully played his part as a link between Anderson, the Cabinet Minister who with Churchill and Cherwell virtually formulated policy, and the teams under Akers who implemented it. Nevertheless, the situation rankled; and years later it was to produce what one colleague described as the only mean act he could ever remember from Appleton. "He chose to base strictly on salary the recommendation for a man loaned from ICI because he did not like the

125

man; so that the award was an OBE when most of us felt CBE would have been better."

The problem of explaining the organisation of Tube Alloys to the British scientists involved was only one of those on which Appleton had to exercise all his talents in the autumn of 1941. There was also that of the French nuclear team, two of whose members had arrived in the summer of 1940 with the precious heavy water — so precious that it had been guarded in the vaults of Windsor Castle before being taken to the Cavendish. Both these men, Lew Kowarski and Hans Halban, had already, in France, lodged patents directly concerned with the making of nuclear weapons. Their feelings about such patents were diametrically opposed — in much the same way as Appleton's and Watson-Watt's views on radar were opposed. And both now had to be brought officially under the wing of Appleton's DSIR. After much discussion, Halban signed a 5-year contract with the DSIR, Kowarski a 2-year one; but Kowarski was unhappy at receiving returns for patents which he had not really wished to lodge. "In March 1944, which was six months before the expiry of the two-year duration, and therefore the earliest moment at which I was allowed to give notice, I declared to Appleton that I wanted to terminate all special returns based on the patents, and that I would prefer the normal status of a temporary Civil Servant", he has since said. And he still remembers how Appleton explained solicitously: "But the contract, and in particular the salary figure, was determined taking into account the advantage accruing to you from the patents." Kowarski grandly replied: "I waive it." When, a few months later, he received a normal contract from Appleton, he found that his salary was in fact to be increased — the result, he still feels, of Appleton's sympathetic belief that there was something inherently wrong in trying to patent the laws of nature.

This was not to be the end of Appleton's problems. Later, when it was decided that work should be started in Canada, Kowarski did not wish to leave England. In the words of the official history, "most of the Cavendish team rose up in wrath and said that they too refused to go. They admired the patience, clarity of thinking and quietness of Kowarski, and affirmed strongly that without him the work carried out in Cambridge would not have been possible. There was much cabling backwards and forwards to

Mr. Akers in Montreal and members of the British Technical Committee, notably Chadwick, tried their hands at peacemaking. In the end Sir Edward Appleton persuaded most of the Cavendish team to sign their contracts and go to Canada while Kowarski's position was discussed further."

"E.V.A.", as he now frequently signed himself, was the ideal man for such persuasions, the patient, imperturbable ironer-out of problems, scientifically irreproachable, personally uncommitted to either side in the arguments. It was he who could write with authority "to Ministers or College Principals or Company Chairmen to press the claims of Tube Alloys" when men were required. He became the channel through which the organisation funnelled its requests for scientists and equipment, and on one famous occasion he was forced to approach his old friend, Sir Noel Ashbridge, by this time Deputy Director-General of the BBC. Appleton had to acquire some important engineering equipment owned by the Corporation, but was unable, for security reasons, to give Ashbridge any idea of what it was required for; Ashbridge, on his part, was forbidden to hand over the equipment until he could give the Director-General full details of where, and for what, it was being lent. Typically, Appleton was able to smooth feelings, to say no more than allowed, and yet get the equipment.

Thus he performed an essential function in an organisation which, it has been officially pointed out, "was admittedly most untidy, with no clear division of function between the head of the DSIR, the Director of Tube Alloys, Professor Chadwick and the Combined Policy representatives in Washington, and no clear line of communication from the responsible minister downwards". This untidiness is underlined by an entry in Appleton's diary for 24 August 1942: "Should not Canada be considered for pilot and whole project"; but at this date Anderson had for some weeks been discussing just such a move with the Canadians themselves.

Appleton, like many other men, including both the Deputy Prime Minister, Mr. Attlee, and the Chiefs of Staff, was kept comparatively in the dark so far as the high-level aspects of Tube Alloys were concerned, and this was exemplified when, in 1943, it was decided to set up in Washington a Combined Policy Committee of United States and British representatives to deal with matters affecting nuclear energy. It had been taken for granted that this post would go to Akers; but the Americans now made it clear that due to his connections with ICI Akers would be *persona non grata* in any position where he would receive technical information—a natural enough reaction in the circumstances but one which cast a totally unwarranted slur on Akers.

Appleton now received a somewhat peremptory order from Sir John Anderson. He was to fly to Washington at once to consult with the Tube Alloys representatives there and to recommend without delay who should have the key British post of technical adviser to the Policy Committee. Thus pitchforked into work for which he had scant briefing, he flew to Washington with Arthur Blok, a senior patents official who had been co-opted into Tube Alloys largely to deal with the controversial French patents; on the delicate matter of selecting a scientist to suit the Americans, Blok could have provided Appleton with little help. This, as it happened, did not matter. By the time that Appleton's plane touched down in the United States, the decision which had brought him from his work for a wartime crossing of the Atlantic had already been taken in Washington by Colonel Llewellin, then Minister of State for Supply in the United States. Appleton's task was merely to recommend whether the appointment should be permanent.

With the signing of the Quebec Agreement which handed over the whole project to the Americans, the importance of Tube Alloys virtually ended. Soon, however, the Allied nuclear enterprise was to re-unite Appleton with his old friend, Niels Bohr, whose voyage from Copenhagen to Sweden and subsequent flight to Britain in a high-flying Mosquito was one of the epic escape stories of the war. When Bohr arrived in England he was formally put under the care of Appleton as Secretary of the DSIR, and stayed in London for a number of weeks, learning of Allied work on the bomb and of Anglo-U.S. relations before moving on to the United States.

Despite the run-down of Tube Alloys which followed transfer of the nuclear weapon work to the United States, Appleton remained nominally in charge of the residual group in England. When, in April 1945, it was agreed that an experimental establishment should be set up in England, it was he who recommended that Cockcroft should run what became

Harwell—a choice of incalculable importance to Britain's post-war development of atomic energy.

When nuclear weapons were eventually used on Japanese cities in August 1945, Appleton appears to have been in the same position as most other men outside a small United States circle—ignorant of the fact that the Japanese were preparing for peace. His reaction was the expected one. He said a few words in a hastily arranged BBC broadcast, and a decade later, in his Reith Lectures, confirmed that he supported the use of the weapons against Japan "on overall humanitarian grounds at that moment of history". Later it appears that he may have developed qualifications about letting the genie out of the box. "But it can be claimed that the advent of the atomic bomb has, at least, pulled the world up sharply and made us all face the stark reality of the consequences of a war in the future," he said to the Bradford Civic Society in 1948. "For we know that the atomic bomb of today cannot represent the most devastating scientific weapon which could be devised for the waging of war. It is only an illustration."

Next to his work within Tube Alloys, Appleton's membership of the Scientific Advisory Committee of the Cabinet would at first glance appear to have provided his most important wartime work outside the DSIR. It seems unlikely that this was so. The Committee's papers have not been made accessible, but the available evidence appears to reinforce Tizard's subsequent opinion that the Committee was "really ineffective". It had been set up in October 1940, the result of a third, almost despairing, effort by the Royal Society to ensure that the nation's scientific expertise should be available at the highest level. Under the chairmanship of Lord Hankey there sat the Royal Society's two secretaries and the secretaries of the DSIR and the Medical and Agricultural Research Councils. Its terms of reference were: "To advise the Government on any scientific problems referred to it; to advise Government departments, when required, on the selection of individuals for particular lines of scientific enquiry or for membership of committees on which scientists are required; and to bring to the notice of the Government promising new scientific or technical developments which may be of importance to the war effort." But the SAC was tolerated by Churchill only on the condition that "we are to have additional support from outside rather than an incursion into our interior", and its overall influence seems to have been marginal rather than significant. Appleton's diaries are studded with the times of its meetings and of the various sub-committees which it set up. It involved him in much talk and, one suspects, a good deal of time-wasting. His real influence was to be exercised elsewhere.

On the outbreak of war there were two fields in which he was pre-eminent—those of the ionosphere in particular and of radio and radar in general. His activities in both were to be affected by what Tizard described as "human considerations". The importance to the war effort of Appleton's speciality—ionospheric investigation—did not lie only in its close links with radar. By September 1939 his discovery of the linkage between radio black-outs and magnetic storms had been considerably extended since it was being appreciated that the state of the ionosphere could seriously affect the RAF's direction-finding equipment which used high-frequency radio; and it was also being realised that some form of prediction service, giving advance warning of oncoming ionospheric conditions, might soon be possible. These facts induced Appleton to suggest informally to the Services, soon after the outbreak of war, that ionospheric forecasting of radio conditions might be useful. It has been claimed that all three Services rejected such proposals, and it is certain that little was immediately done. Meanwhile, the RAF's navigational techniques continued to be confused by ionospheric conditions. The situation rose to a head when a number of planes, destined for a leaflet raid on Germany, flew instead straight up the North Sea until they ran out of petrol.

Eventually the Services accepted the need for ionospheric forecasting. However, they turned not to Appleton but, naturally enough in some ways, to the Marconi Group which at Great Baddow outside Chelmsford had been engaged for some years in ionospheric research and, more particularly, in a study of its relationship with long-distance high-frequency radio propagation. At the head of this group stood T. L. Eckersley, the radio expert whose experiments of 1920 had shown the existence of "some upper conducting layer of the atmosphere". Appleton had never had particularly friendly relations with Eckersley and had disagreed with him on a number of scientific matters. His comment on a letter of Eckers-

PLATE 9A. A group in Appleton's rooms in St. John's, Cambridge, about 1938, showing Appleton seventh from right; J. A. Ratcliffe, sixth from right; and R. G. Piggott, extreme left.

PLATE 9B. (*right*) Edward Appleton, left, and Robert Naismith digging foundations for the aerial mast stays at Simavik in northern Norway.

PLATE 10. The first Lady Appleton and her elder daughter, Margery
(*by courtesy of* Mason & Co., Cambridge).

PLATE 11. The Cavendish Research Staff, 1938, showing in front row Sir J. J. Thomson, sixth from left; Lawrence Bragg, seventh from left; and Edward Appleton, eighth from left (*by courtesy of* Hill & Saunders).

PLATE 12.   Presentation to Sir Edward and Lady Appleton on his resignation from the Department of Scientific and Industrial Research, 1949.

PLATE 13. Sir Edward with his younger daughter, Rosalind, relaxing at the piano
(*by courtesy of* Associated Press).

PLATE 14A. Receiving the Freedom of the city of Bradford, 1947, from the Lord Mayor, Alderman T. I. Clough (by courtesy of *Yorkshire Observer*).

PLATE 14B. (*left*) Receiving the Nobel Prize for Physics from King Gustav of Sweden, 1947 (*by courtesy of* A B Reportagebild).

PLATE 15. Giving the Presidential address at the September, 1953, meeting of the British Association for the Advancement of Science; to his left, Sir Henry Tizard.

PLATE 16.   At his desk in Edinburgh University, working on the Reith Lectures
(by courtesy of *The Scotsman*).

ley's which he passed on to Slough before the war, "... quite wrong—as usual", typified his attitude, a slightly curious one towards a scientist who had been elected to the Royal Society on three separate counts—as physicist, mathematician, and engineer. It is clear that contacts between Eckersley and Appleton were slight throughout the war; that this was not entirely due to the mass of work on which both were engaged; and that the coolness between them was, as much as anything else, the cause of Appleton's lack of contact with the Inter-Services Ionosphere Bureau set up jointly by the Air Ministry and the Admiralty at Great Baddow in 1941 with Eckersley as Chief Scientific Adviser.

This was an unfortunate situation, since the Radio Research Station at Slough continued to issue its own ionospheric forecasts not only to the Serivices but to the Dominions. The two predictions were, moreover, not always the same, and late in 1943 New Zealand pointed out that while two sets of ionospheric forecasts were being issued from two British stations less than 50 miles apart, these did not always agree. To deal with the situation, a meeting was called at the Admiralty, and here it was resolved that a liaison party consisting of two members of the Radio Research Board and two from the Inter-Services Ionospheric Bureau "should consider the technical questions raised in detail". The impression given is that of armistice discussions. At the end of the meeting "Sir Edward Appleton pointed out that, after the war, RRB would again be solely responsible for supplying the Services with the fundamental ionospheric measurements in this country", a statement received with surprise by the Services who had not yet decided the issue. Appleton's attitude can be gauged by the fact that when, after the war, he wrote an account of Britain's war-time ionospheric prediction work for the first post-war meeting of URSI, no mention at all was made of the ISI—"a grave omission" as he later admitted.

Occupied as he was with so many aspects of war-time science, Appleton's at least partial isolation from some of the country's most important ionospheric work was not as troublesome as it might otherwise have been. He did, moreover, find time to continue a good deal of his own original investigations with such colleagues as Piggott and W. J. G. Beynon, a young physicist from the National Physical Laboratory.

In the allied field of radar the position was more complicated, and only a lucky combination of circumstances enabled Appleton to deploy his scientific expertise here with the freedom which it deserved. It has already been stated that at the time of Munich he had been earmarked for radio work within the Air Ministry, and it is at least a strong assumption that this was ruled out by the relationships between himself and Watson-Watt. These formed the Achilles heel of the reasoned and impartial, the scientifically objective, man that was the essential Appleton. Of the dismay which this weakness sometimes created there can be no doubt. Appleton would, for instance, carry about with him copies of his early papers and with little encouragement would produce them at war-time meetings to illustrate his own part in the long chain of events which led to radar. Thus his quarrel with Watson-Watt embarrassed many of his friends, and it handicapped the war effort in a sphere where it could least afford to be handicapped—that of technological innovation. This might, but for one factor, have shunted Appleton's knowledge into a sideline of war-time radar development. That factor was the extent to which radar grew with the war; for the field became big enough to contain even Appleton and Watson-Watt. By the middle of 1941 there were, in fact, more than a dozen separate committees, sub-committees, and other groups dealing with RDF as it was then still called, among them the Ministry of Supply's RDF Applications Committee, an off-shoot of the Ministry's Advisory Council on Scientific Research and Technical Development. With Appleton as chairman and a membership which included Blackett, Cockcroft, Oliphant, Watson-Watt, and Smith-Rose, the head of the Radio Research Station, it met for the first time on 8 March 1940. Its brief was "to consider and advise on the application of RDF to military purposes", and it was later to be suggested by the Air Ministry that it took a liberal view of the word "military", extending its advice and activities into matters that went far beyond what was intended to be the purely Army significance of the word. This was hardly surprising in view of the ability and determination of its members. In October 1940 this committee decided—according to the official history—that the maximum activity in radar development should be concentrated on wavelengths below 10 cm, and that 50 cm work should continue only as an insurance against possible failure at

10 cm. Appleton, its chairman, is sometimes given the main credit for the decision from which were to spring the short-wave radar devices which were to have such a crucial effect on the war. This view is strongly contested by more than one of those closely involved. This flat contradiction of what happened does not stem entirely from the bitter animosities aroused among those who could not avoid taking sides in the Appleton–Watson-Watt debate. War-time radar development rested not only on an interlocking tangle of committees, ranging in importance from chiefs of staff committees downwards but also on the work of brilliant teams at more than one research station—notably the Telecommunications Research Establishment under A. P. Rowe which still rarely gets the credit it deserves—and on the independent personal intervention of Lord Cherwell or of those who gained his support. These factors, combined with the passage of three decades and the dearth of original documents, provide a genuine enough explanation for disagreement; what Tizard called the "human considerations" merely add the edge to it. Perhaps the fairest and most objective summing-up—although it may not seem so to those whose experience was limited entirely to the scientific and the operational side—is provided by Sir Bernard Lovell whose small group was so largely responsible for the development of H₂S, one of the devices which exploited short waves to such good effect. "It is my opinion," he says, "that Cherwell was the decisive voice urging the production of H₂S which really gave the impetus which resulted so quickly in the general availability of centimetric equipment. These comments do not, of course, exclude the possibility that Appleton may have been a decisive influence at the earlier stages in 1940 in persuading people that the vital fundamental researches on the magnetron should continue. . . . The actual acute operational situation which existed at that time in airborne radar for night fighter interception was such that a man like Appleton may have been able to see the solution much more clearly than many others."

Whatever the exact influence of Appleton on short-wave development—and it seems certain that this influence would have been less powerful than that of "the RDF circus" as he called it—there is no doubt of his influence in other radar fields.

Thus there was Appleton's Ultra Short Wave Panel, a small group that was correctly the Ultra Short Wave Panel of the RDF Applications Committee of the Advisory Council for Scientific Research and Technical Development of the Ministry of Supply. This had been set up after one of the coastal radar stations working on very short wavelengths had found itself able to follow ships well beyond the horizon. The same station also reported picking up radar echoes from the coast of France—at about four times the normal range. "The explanation soon became clear," said Appleton later. "It turned out that, during still weather, the lower layers of the atmosphere exert a most favourable influence on the propagation of radio waves—so that their track through the air is not straight, but curved like the surface of the sea. Nature has been kind in bending the waves the right way—downwards instead of upwards. But of course these favourable conditions do not occur all the time and it is necessary, for practical purposes, to predict when they are likely to occur"—a necessity which led to the development of radio-meteorology.

The panel was mainly composed of young scientists who used to boast that it consisted entirely of scientific workers, officials being barred. "That *I* personally might have been classed in the latter category was generously overlooked," commented Appleton. To it there were reported, for the rest of the war, all the unaccountable points of scientific interest in the ultra-short-wave field which occurred either in experimental work or at the operational radar stations which were soon to be scattered across the world. A number of interesting reports came its way; one, which was to be of great importance to post-war science, was of a curious radio noise, noted when 5-metre radar sets working with anti-aircraft guns were turned towards the sun. "I well remember," said Appleton later, "that we recalled at the meeting at which this was reported, that it was most probably connected with a curious hiss which wireless amateurs had reported to me around the year 1937 and which we had linked up with the occurrence of sun-spots."

The Ultra Short Wave Panel was yet one more group of specialists dealing with radar. By the summer of 1941 there were more than a dozen of them, ranging in importance from the Air Ministry's Inter-Service RDF Committee, which had been set up in 1938, and Appleton's Applications Committee, to much smaller bodies. And it was now that Lord Hankey recommended to the chiefs of staff that the whole convoluted maze of radar research and policy groups should be reformed, and much of the existing work brought under a committee of their own organisation. This was to be the RDF Policy Committee, under which there was to be a technical sub-committee; and its setting-up brought an exchange of letters between Appleton and Tizard which illuminates, better than anything else, the relationship existing between Appleton and Watson-Watt, the difficulties which this created, and the way in which it affected war-time organisation.

Tizard, by this time a member of the Air Council and unofficial adviser to the Minister for Aircraft Production, was in a strong position to influence events. He was eventually to become the new committee's chairman, and on first hearing the change mooted had written a long advisory note to Air Marshal Sir Charles Portal, Chief of Air Staff. For while Appleton's name had been put forward as a potential member, Watson-Watt's had not. "I see no good reason for the inclusion of Sir Edward," said Tizard, pointing out that the Committee would deal with policy rather than with technical matters, and that if it was really thought necessary to bring a technical man on to the main committee, then the chairman of the sub-committee was the obvious choice, Sir Frank Smith being the "obvious" man for such a post. Watson-Watt protested to Portal, and Portal asked Tizard to deal with the matter. Then, on 21 July, Tizard wrote to Appleton.

"I only heard recently," he began, "that a Chiefs of Staff RDF Policy Committee is being set up to replace the original Inter-Services Committee, and that this new Policy Committee was going to have a technical sub-committee to advise it with rather wide terms of reference.

"Trouble has arisen about the Policy Committee since it was decided, as Watson-Watt has pointed out with some justification, that as you are nominated a member of the Policy Committee and that he is not even, in the first place, a member of the technical committee, he must interpret this as a vote of no confidence. He saw the Chief of Air Staff about this, and the C.A.S. in his turn has asked for my written views.

"I agree with Watson-Watt and his general contention. . . . I have . . . said that I thought it was a mistake in the circumstances to put you on

135

originally as a member of the Policy Committee. [Incidentally it has got Smith's back up also.] It is a great pity that the war is so affected by these human considerations, but there it is.

"I have told CAS that as the object of the Policy Committee is to determine policy and not to indulge in amateur talks about science, I thought it might be wise to have no scientific member, except the Chairman of the Technical Sub-Committee which would be advising the Policy Committee, and who would be on as Chairman and not in his individual capacity; and I have also advised that the terms of reference of the Policy Committee should omit any reference to research and development, and that it should be made clear that the object of the Policy Committee is to determine the needs of the Services and not to discuss or try to influence as a committee the methods by which those needs are met.

"I have then said that the technical committe should act as technical adviser on any point the Policy Committee refers to it and should co-ordinate work in the different Departments which is designed to fulfil the needs expressed by the Policy Committee. If that is accepted, I have suggested that the membership of the technical committee should include yourself, Smith, Watson-Watt, Cockcroft and the appropriate member of the Admiralty Signals Experimental Establishment.

"I thought you would like to know all this. There is such an air of intrigue about RDF development nowadays that I prefer you to know exactly what I am advising, even if you should not altogether agree with it. But do let me know if you agree or not."

Five days later Appleton explained his position.

"My dear Tizard," he wrote on the 26th, "Do, please, forgive a late reply to your letter of July 21st. I've been spending two days at Signal School with Fowler and other members of the Admiralty Panel.

"I agree with a very great deal of what you say and am glad you wrote because it gives me an opportunity to make the full facts, so far as I am concerned, known to you. I understand that the first meeting of the Policy Committee was tentative and exploratory and that I was put on because I was Chairman of the only RDF Committee in existence. This is confirmed by the fact that the papers for the meeting were actually addressed to that Chairman and delivered at the Ministry of Supply.

"At the meeting I said that this civilian membership would not do and proposed (1) that Smith should be made Chairman of the Technical Committee and (2) that the Chairman of that Committee should be made a member of the Policy Committee. I allowed my own membership to continue because I understood that the presence of the Chairman of both the Technical Committees (the existing one and the one to be formed) was considered likely to be helpful.

"As you know I'm not looking for work; nor do I want to get involved in the RDF circus of 'political' self-seekers. (There is much to be said for a ring side seat). I would willingly therefore withdraw, leaving the Chairman of the Technical Committee as the sole attendant adviser of the Policy Committee.

"It never occurred to me that Watson-Watt would be hurt about not being included in the Policy Committee. ... As an adviser to the Air Ministry his job is to advise the Air Ministry representative on the Policy Committee. In other words his job ought to be done before that representative attended; though no doubt he might attend meetings as an 'aide-de-memoire'. After all, you well know that at inter-service meetings proportionate representation is desirable and I was given to understand that my detached position alone justified my attendance.

"If I had known originally that my innocent acceptance of a summons to a meeting would have led to the criticism of my membership described in your second paragraph, I might have hesitated a great deal. ... since you say you agree with the sufferer, you are encouraging it at a time when such things ought not to matter. I will readily retire from the Policy Committee if it is considered that I should do so in the interests of the work; but I suggest to you that Watson-Watt is using your influence to get me ejected because his feelings are slighted.

"Again the Technical Committee was given a symmetrical Ministry representation at first (MAP, M of S and Admiralty) the way being left for others to be added. It is quite certain that Watson-Watt would have been put on. I should myself have suggested it. Like you I recognise his great qualities and, though I've more than once had my suggestion that he should be put on a purely technical committee met with a 'Why?', I think his general co-ordinating knowledge acquired through the years very useful indeed.

"I don't understand your phrase about 'amateur talks about science'." A few days later Tizard provided the disarming reply, explaining that his remark about amateur talks on science referred to Service enthusiasts, and concluding: "What an infernal nuisance all this is! In my bad moments I feel that too many people are more interested in themselves than in winning the war. I can say this to you because it does not apply."

Although Appleton renewed his offer to withdraw his membership, he did not finally do so, and in the end the Committee included himself, Watson-Watt, Sir Frank Smith, and two representatives from each of the three Services. Whether the detailed arguments as to who should or should not sit on the Committee were really worth while is a moot point. As Tizard, its chairman, was later to protest, it was typical that development of H_2S, the radar bombing aid, was given top priority without the Committee being consulted — "the matter was settled apparently on recommendations of, or pressure from, Lord Cherwell. ...."

However, Appleton's membership of what was, despite its limitations, a chiefs of staff committee no doubt helped to maintain his interest not only in radar itself but in its genesis, and this may account for his request to the Admiralty, in the autumn of 1944, for a copy of Alder's secret patent for radar lodged in February 1928. He appears not to have seen it before, studied it carefully one may assume, and kept it among his papers.

Appleton maintained a number of links with the military, as distinct from the civilian, side of the scientific war. These links were reinforced by contacts with the intelligence authorities whom he advised on the technical interception of enemy radio messages — the man involved giving Appleton technical details of how messages were intercepted without divulging what they contained — and by contacts with the Norwegian resistance movement. He had maintained links with Tromso observatory following his return from the Polar Year expedition and he was, therefore, one of the relatively few men in England with a knowledge of northern Norway.

This knowledge was utilised in recruiting Norwegian scientists for work in Britain, an operation that had begun with an invitation from Appleton to Herman Dahl, a Norwegian radio worker. Dahl arrived in England across the North Sea in April 1942. "I was immediately taken to see Sir Edward," he says. "He received me in very friendly fashion, and explained that there was a shortage of scientific manpower. Afterwards we had a meeting with several people, including Frederick [later Sir Frederick] Brundrett. It was agreed that I should be enlisted in the Norwegian Forces and then transferred for British service, to carry out research work. It was also agreed that I should try to find other Norwegians able to do the same work. Eventually, there were 22 of us working in British research establishments. From talks with Sir Edward I gained the impression that he was behind the idea, since he found it inefficient for Allied scientists to be kept in their own national forces where they could not use all their abilities. He particularly liked to extract scientists from German-dominated territories, since this was a double gain."

Among these Norwegians whom Appleton helped to "extract" was Olaf Devik who arrived in London from Norway in March 1943 to work on the problem of how best to restore and develop Norwegian universities and research institutions after the war. He often discussed this with Appleton, whom he had known in 1932, and it was to Appleton that he turned in the autumn of 1944.

"The German forces in Northern Norway had started a scorched earth policy and the frontier of devastation proceeded southwards," he says. "On the 27th of November 1944, a messenger from Tromso, consul Gudleif Holmboe, arrived in London with the task of presenting the urgency of stopping this tragic threat to all of Northern Norway. How to influence the British war strategy would be a problem, and in the subsequent deliberations I mentioned to members of the Norwegian Government the possibility of informing Lord Cherwell, the personal adviser to the Prime Minister.

"Knowing that Sir Edward knew Lord Cherwell personally, I talked the matter over with Sir Edward, who was immediately willing to co-operate. The result was that Sir Edward and myself had an appointment with Lord Cherwell at 10 Downing Street on the evening of November 30, where we had the opportunity of presenting the disastrous facts which had brought Mr. Holmboe from Tromso as a special messenger. The following day my verbal report was given to the proper members of the Norwegian Government. Mr. Holmboe could return with the impression that his information might have found its way to the Inner Circle, thanks to the co-operation of Sir Edward."

Help was a two-way affair, and Appleton's links with Norway were to involve him with one of the most famous incidents of the war – the destruction of the *Tirpitz*. The Norwegian ionospheric group attached to the observatory of Tromso had continued work until the German occupation of April 1940. Investigations were then taken over by a small German group which continued routine observations from the Auroral observatory and passed them on to the German equivalent of the Inter-Services Ionospheric Bureau working at Great Baddow. During 1944 these investigations were extended by the erection of a pulse transmitter working on a fixed frequency of about 2 Mc/s. It was set up about a mile from the main observatory and mid-way between this building and the hamlet of Hakoybotn about 3 miles from Tromso. Shortly afterwards the *Tirpitz*, by this time the last of the German battleships, steamed into Tromso, having already been damaged by RAF attacks. Then she was taken to Hakoybotn and moored for repairs. A few days later a member of the Norwegian resistance sent the following message to London: "Ionospheric pulse transmitter working on 2 Mc/s placed two km from *Tirpitz* is working continuously; ideal for direction finding; please consult Professor Appleton on this matter."

The *Tirpitz* was again attacked. Three years later, when Appleton was visiting Norway after receiving the Nobel Prize for Physics in Stockholm, he was asked by the Norwegians whether he ever received the message, but felt himself unable to answer. Ironically, the news would probably have been handled by the Inter-Services Bureau at Great Baddow.

The final destruction of the *Tirpitz* came within weeks of the Allied liberation of Eindhoven in Holland, the site of the giant Philips factory which was a major target of Allied interest. Appleton himself visited Brussels, where he met his old friend Van der Pol who had been successfully hamstringing German activities for years. He was preceded in Eindhoven by Watson-Watt, who, due to the purely fortuitous activities of a British intelligence unit, found himself somewhat embarrassed. During the German occupation various Dutch employees at Philips had crossed the Channel, informed the British of what was going on, and had then returned to Eindhoven. In England they had been interrogated by a youngish man; he did not claim to be Sir Edward Appleton, but his name was Appleton and to him the good Dutchmen told all they knew. Months later they could be heard in Eindhoven, explaining to Watson-Watt that they had already told all they knew, in England, to Appleton.

Sir Edward's most intriguing link with German ionospheric work came soon after the end of the war when his colleague, W. R. Piggott, returned from a short visit to Germany with the suggestion that the entire German unit under Professor Dieminger, then in Austria, might with good effect be moved some hundreds of miles north-west into the British Zone, and set up as a continuing centre for ionospheric research. Appleton agreed, somewhat reluctantly, and stressing that he would have to disown all knowledge of the operation if anything went wrong. As it was, everything went right, and under Piggott's direction the entire laboratory was moved in convoy to the outskirts of Göttingen and set up under British control.

CHAPTER 9

1946–1949: THE POST-WAR PAUSE

IN AT least one respect, the end of the war found Appleton in a more fortunate position than many of his scientific colleagues. Whereas they had been concentrating entirely on the application of science to Service problems he had been able, during the previous three years, to devote an increasing amount of thought to post-war problems. Thus the outbreak of peace brought no vacuum, no sense of anti-climax, such as it brought to many of the scientists who had been involved, directly and exclusively, in the use of their ideas in the day-by-day struggle in the air or on the seas. Whereas their jobs had ended overnight, leaving them with the sometimes awkward problems of readjustment, Appleton's flowed directly on from war into peace. His sense of this was well brought out in a letter he wrote years later to Lord Bridges, emphasising that it was "a fortunate thing that Anderson was in charge of Government civil science when the application of science to industry was recognised as a necessity. Prompted by him," Appleton went on, "I 'stumped' the country—this was his own later phrase describing this particular exercise—using the scientific successes in war as an example of what might accrue in peace."

It was thus partly to explain the more important role that the staff of DSIR would play in the future, that in the second half of 1945 Appleton began a major tour of the Department's stations. At each he explained what the planned expansion would mean; and at each he was quick to look for, and to spot, the men who could and should take a major part in this. At the same time he stressed that wherever security allowed the staff should describe and publish the war-time work that had contributed so much to victory. Appleton knew better than most how great this contribution was, not only through such spectacular examples as radar, the jet-engine, and the host of ingenious devices which had enabled the Allies to return via the Normandy beaches, but in a multitude of more hum-drum ways. The more important work, he felt, should be simply described for the ordinary public, and under his encouragement two scientific authors from outside the Department—J. G. Crowther and Robert Whiddington, the latter Cavendish Professor of Physics at Leeds University—were commissioned to write what became *Science at War*, an account that concentrated on radar, the atomic bomb, and the war at sea.

Appleton's plans for the post-war expansion of the DSIR were not to be entirely satisfied, and it is difficult not to feel that he mentally placed some of the blame for this on the politics of the Socialist Government. However, it seems clear that for Morrison, Lord President in the July 1945 Government, he had—despite reports to the contrary—considerable admiration, describing him on one occasion as the best Minister he had served under and by far the most able politician he had known. For other members of the new Government he had more qualified admiration, and he long remembered the occasion on which Ernest Bevin, then Foreign Secretary, told him that if scientists only worked properly then Britain would be able to increase the efficiency of the country's power stations to 100 per cent. "I was obliged to tell the Minister," he later noted, "that God had decided that this was not possible and that He had formulated His decision in the second law of thermodynamics."

While Appleton was to be intimately connected with post-war restructuring of the scientific establishment in Britain, both this and his Presidency of URSI linked him with the reconstruction of science on the Continent. Thus during the later 1940's his already full schedules were still further swollen by numerous journeys abroad. The plans for one of these helped to produce the Mixed Commission on the Ionosphere. In the summer of 1945 Appleton had been due to attend a conference in Lyons at which the post-war reconstruction of French science was to be discussed. At the last moment he found himself unable to attend and suggested that his collabo-

Sir Edward Appleton

rator Beynon should go instead. There might, he added, be talk of setting up some joint body from among the four international scientific bodies concerned with ionospheric studies—those dealing with radio, with geodesy and geophysics, with astronomy, and with pure and applied physics. If this was the case, Beynon was to take note of what was being proposed and to act accordingly. Beynon duly did as suggested, with the result that when the Mixed Commission on the Ionosphere was subsequently founded by the International Council of Scientific Unions, he became secretary and Appleton became chairman. It is a measure of the Commission's success that of the dozen unsolved problems which were presented by Appleton and Beynon at this first meeting, five had been solved and another four partly solved by the time of Appleton's death in 1965. The Commission was also, and perhaps most important of all, to play a vital part in officially proposing the International Geophysical Year of 1957/58.

In 1946 Appleton's presidency of URSI took him to Paris where the organisation's General Assembly was held after a lapse of eight years—eight years during which war had made the major nations realise how vital to their radio communications was a knowledge of the ionosphere. Most of them had set up their own networks of ionospheric sounding stations, and in his presidential address Appleton voiced the hope that "now that the war is over, and it is no longer necessary to plan the siting of ionospheric stations throughout the world on strategic considerations, it would be possible to site our stations more nearly according to scientific requirements".

Later in the year he was invited to the United States—where at the Massachusetts Institute of Technology he delivered the first of the Arthur Dehon Little lectures, on "Science, Government, and Industry"—and to Canada. As usual he took care to prepare his speeches in advance. "I'm told there will be the usual dinner associated with the lecture," he wrote to the Master of St. John's, "and thought of taking with me a copy of the poem which W. E. Heitland wrote in 1886 to celebrate the breakfasting of Oliver Wendell Holmes in our own Combination Room! I hope you approve of this claiming of a link between Boston and St. John's." He used the poem to good effect in Boston and Toronto—and in both places kept a watchful eye open for Johnians. "The Gloverian spell still exists in East-

144

ern Canada, emanating from Queen's, Kingston," he wrote to the Master on his return to England. "To have known T. R. Glover is, in so many cases, an introduction to friendship. I saw more than one Johnian tie and in each case found the wearer eager for College news." Here, as in more than one of Appleton's other letters, is a hint of what is sometimes claimed to have been one ambition of his later life, to become Master of St. John's.

The following year began badly with the death of his father—news of which came as Appleton was sorting out the Christmas cards from well-known people which he regularly sent on to his parents. The sudden death was doubly regrettable since only a few months later Appleton was elected an Honorary Freeman of Bradford, a recognition which would have crowned the father's pride in his son's achievements.

In the same year Appleton was invited to give the Halley Lecture at Oxford and the Rede Lecture at Cambridge on "Radar development and scientific radio research" and "Terrestrial magnetism and the ionosphere" respectively. In 1946 he was created a Knight Grand Cross of the Order of the British Empire, and in the following year awarded the US Medal of Merit, the American civilian award, and the Norwegian Cross of Freedom, as well as being made an Officer of the French Legion of Honour. Two years later he was appointed by the Pope to the Pontifical Academy of Science, and in 1950 was awarded the Albert Medal of the Royal Society of Arts for outstanding services to science and industrial research.

All this was overshadowed by something considerably more important—the Nobel Prize for Physics, awarded in 1947 for Appleton's ionospheric researches in the 1920's. The announcement came in mid-November, and early the next month he travelled to Sweden with his wife and younger daughter. The ceremony, in the Stockholm Concert Hall, where the prizes are awarded by the King on the anniversary of the death of dynamite's inventor, was the kind that delighted him. "Nothing seems further removed from the modern, austere and good-humoured laboratories where the great discoveries are made," it has been written of the occasion. "The prize-winners sit in a row, cheerful or nervous in evening dress—though it is mid-afternoon—while their work is explained in popular science lectures to the royal family and the diplomatic corps. The sense of ritual is enhanced by the use of a cryptic language, Swedish.

145

White-gowned students in the gallery sing in chorus. Trumpeters blow a fanfare for each laureate as his turn comes at last to step down to the king."

Since the awards are announced in alphabetical order, Appleton was first to receive the medal, the diploma, and the envelope officially telling him that he could collect the prize money of about £10,000 from the Nobel Foundation. As the announcement was made, with its description of the vertical-probing of the ionosphere, his daughter was heard to comment: "There must be something in Daddy after all."

In his Nobel Lecture, Appleton reviewed the exploration of the ionosphere since he had first discovered its height in 1924. He outlined the connection between the theoretical and the practical applications of the research which he and others had carried out. He explained how it was now possible to forecast "ionospheric weather" some time ahead, and he ended on a typical note by stressing that "scientific work conducted in the first instance with the object of exploring the wonders of the world around us, is now indicating how nation can speak unto nation with greater clarity and certainty".

That evening he and his wife and daughter attended the Nobel Banquet at which each of the winners had to speak; as usual Appleton had taken considerable care in preparing his material. He wanted, as was customary in his speeches, to tell a story — one which would have a scientific ring and which would be easily understood in Sweden. He had such a story in mind and he passed a slip of paper to Lady Appleton, who was seated next to the Crown Prince, later King Gustavus VI Adolphus, asking her if she thought he should tell it. The Crown Prince, who saw the paper, encouraged her to agree.

Shortly afterwards, Sir Edward rose. Having pointed out the close relationship between the Royal Society and the Swedish Academy of Sciences, he expressed his gratitude to the Academy and underlined the importance of scientific research.

"Ladies and Gentlemen," he continued, "you should not however overrate scientific methods, as you will learn from the story of a man who started an investigation to find out why people get drunk. I believe this tale might interest you here in Sweden.

The Post-war Pause

"This man offered some of his friends one evening a drink consisting of a certain amount of whisky and a certain amount of soda water and in due course observed the results. The next evening he gave the same friends another drink, of brandy and soda water in the same proportion as the previous night. And so it went on for two more days but with rum and soda water, and gin and soda water. The results were always the same.

"He then applied scientific methods, used his sense of logic and drew the only possible conclusion—that the cause of the intoxication must have been the common substance: namely *the soda water!*"

Appleton was pleased but a little surprised at the huge success of the story. Only later did he learn that the Crown Prince drank only soda water—"one of those unexpected bonuses which even the undeserving get from Providence from time to time", as he put it.

With the celebrations duly finished, the Appletons moved on to Norway, Sir Edward meeting again the men who had worked with him in 1932 and some of those who throughout the war had sent scientific recruits to England. It was not only Appleton himself who was popular. So was his daughter, the Rosalind whose "slight naughtiness" always delighted her father. She captivated him as though, somehow, she represented all the things he had never dared to be. When, in England, his wife was unable to accompany him to one Royal Institution meeting, it was Rosalind who turned up instead—and dressed so entrancingly that it was soberly reported that Appleton's Windmill Girl daughter had turned up in her Windmill Girl costume. He loved it; and he loved it when, served with a drink in a hotel that was too weak to suit her, she opened her straw shopping basket, produced a bottle of gin, and proceeded to strengthen the drink to her liking.

The Appletons returned to England shortly before Christmas, Sir Edward remembering to bring for his office colleagues presents of goods that were still in short supply, and then replying by hand to the scores of congratulatory messages which had followed the Nobel Prize publicity.

The bulk of the Department's post-war expansion and reorganisation was by this time well in hand, but Appleton's status was soon drawing down on to his shoulders a volume of work that continued to hamper his ionospheric researches. There was, for instance, his chairmanship of a

Sir Edward Appleton

BBC committee set up in May 1948, which was to affect the development of radio and television during the following years but was virtually unknown to the public. This was the Scientific Advisory Committee—later re-named the Engineering Advisory Committee when a scientific committee was set up to deal with the content of scientific programmes. The brainchild of Sir Noel Ashbridge, its formal function was "to advise on the BBC's scientific research and its correlation with external activities in the same field". With Appleton as chairman, Cockcroft as vice-chairman, and other members who included Willis Jackson, Sir Charles Darwin, and Dr. Smith-Rose, the Committee met three or four times a year. The BBC's engineering staff told the Committee what it was doing and asked their advice; the members of the Committee asked questions in their turn, discussed the problems raised, and when necessary criticised them from the viewpoint of men outside the BBC. The whole field of scientific research was covered, including the training and recruitment not only of the fifty or so top scientists employed but also of the hundreds of technicians required.

Appleton enjoyed this particular committee work more than most, especially the visits which members made to the BBC research establishment at Kingswood Warren. His common sense was remembered as much as his technical knowledge, as when the proposed introduction of regular television raised the question of which of two systems should be used. Committee members were fairly evenly split into those who recommended the United States system of asymmetric sidebands which would allow of five channels being used; and those who preferred the double sideband system which would apparently accommodate only four channels. Appleton thought it over and then pointed out, to the general surprise, that the problem was not an "either/or" question at all; and that it would, in fact, be possible to accommodate in the available waveband four asymmetric sidebands and a London Programme broadcast on the double sideband system. And he pointed out that when, after a few years, it would probably be necessary to replace existing sets, London could be changed to the asymmetric sideband system.

It was the Engineering Advisory Committee which stressed, as far back as 1949, "the desirability of extending the work of appraisal to colour television". It instituted BBC training scholarships for scientists and technologists — partly on Appleton's recommendation — and it was very largely responsible for the whole framework of technical innovation on which the BBC services were built during the immediate post-war years.

This strengthening of Appleton's ties with the BBC was one factor which led to his being co-opted a few years later for a task which demanded the wisdom and tact of Solomon. This was nothing less, in effect, than adjudicating between the rival attitudes of the Foreign Office and the Post Office. The problem concerned the wavebands on which short-wave broadcasts were made. While partly a legacy of the 1939–45 war, it was more importantly a result of current affairs since it revolved around the degree of provision to be made for high frequencies to be used for propaganda in the "cold war".

Short-wave transmissions had been started experimentally by the BBC as far back as 1929, and three years later a worldwide service had been inaugurated. Other countries followed suit and it was soon clear that unless international regulations were laid down and followed, the result would be chaos; the International Radio Regulations were accordingly revised at a conference held in Cairo in 1938, a date that was hardly propitious. The following year the BBC began non-English broadcasting on short waves, and with the outbreak of war Britain, together with the other combatants, tended to put operational efficiency above international regulations. Short-wave transmissions proliferated — in the Services, for communicating with resistance movements, for disseminating propaganda; so did methods of jamming such broadcasts, while to conventional chaos the exponents of the "radio war", which played such a big part in the struggle for air supremacy, brought their own ingenious devices. By the outbreak of peace the regulations decided upon at Cairo, still legally the basis for short-wave broadcasting, were widely ignored. Recommendations had been made at a Mexico City conference in 1944, but neither the United States nor Russia implemented them, and the growth of the cold war in the later 1940's made it unlikely that they would. In 1947 a conference held in Atlantic City under the auspices of the International Telecommunications Union drew up fresh recommendations, and it was hoped that these would be ratified a few years later.

It was at this stage, late in 1950, that Appleton was called in. For while the GPO felt it best to support the Atlantic City recommendations, which would have meant the abandoning of many wavelengths used by the BBC, the Foreign Office was reluctant to follow this policy without further investigation. The Postmaster-General, Mr. Ness Edwards, and the Foreign Secretary, Mr. Ernest Bevin, decided that the best way of deciding the matter would be to have it reviewed by someone outside the government machine; someone who had the necessary technical knowledge yet who would assess impartially the claims and counter-claims of all those deeply engaged in the propaganda war. Again, as so often in the previous hot war, Appleton was an obvious choice.

He willingly agreed to the task, and early in January began moving through what he later called "the labyrinths of these complicated matters". The ministries and other government departments involved, the Services, and the British Joint Communications–Electronics Board, all submitted their proposals for or against implementation of the new table of wavelengths proposed at Atlantic City. Two assessors helped Appleton work his way through the maze, and a few weeks later he presented his report. The nub of it was that "world-wide implementation of the new table would be in the best interests of the U.K.", that "order should be restored to the radio spectrum", even though he recommended an ingenious series of limitations and qualifying proposals which would, he believed, safeguard Britain's position whatever happened.

While advising the BBC, running the DSIR, coping with the large volume of work involved in his presidency of URSI, and attending the meetings of the University Grants Committee of which his government post made him an *ex officio* member, Appleton also continued with ionospheric research. Sometimes he could encourage this from his official position and soon after the war backed what became known as the Canterbury Plains Project. This was an investigation of the curious bending effect which the troposphere exerted on radio propagation in one specific part of New Zealand. Interest in it had first arisen in Rowe's Telecommunication Research Establishment, and eventually a small team of men was seconded to the DSIR. The work involved the use of two RAF aircraft which were to be flown out to New Zealand, and it had been expected in the early stages that the Air Ministry would give the venture all aid. What is remembered two decades after is that while the Air Ministry help was qualified, Appleton from the DSIR pushed through the enterprise with vigour.

Much of his own personal ionospheric research consisted of developing or further investigating phenomena which had arisen directly from war-time work, a classic example being Appleton's own discovery of the geomagnetic anomaly. It was well known that the characteristics of the F_2-Layer in the northern hemisphere — including its height and the critical frequency of the radio waves which would be reflected by it — were different from those of the southern hemisphere. It had, moreover, been assumed that the change from one set of characteristics to another took place roughly in the area of the geographical equator which divides the two hemispheres. Now throughout the latter part of the war ionospheric data was being reported to Slough from many parts of the world, and Appleton naturally took a more than casual interest in this. One day he noticed something which he could not explain. "Baton Rouge and Delhi, although situated on practically the same geographic latitude, reported widely different values of F_2," he later wrote. "I stupidly questioned the accuracy of the Delhi values, by cable, and got an abrupt reply! I think their professional indignation was based on the fact that I had not questioned the accuracy of Baton Rouge at the same time." Both sets of figures were, in fact, correct, even though they did not fit the accepted theory. Appleton then worked out the figures involved, using not the geographical latitudes of the two stations, but their magnetic latitudes. This time the figures fitted. Subsequent work confirmed what he had suspected — that the change-over from one set of characteristics to another took place during day-time in a region more coincident with the magnetic equator than with the geographical one, thus showing that the layer must be strongly influenced by the earth's magnetic field.

Another anomaly in the F_2-Layer that he had recently been investigating was what became known as horizontal drift, a possibility first suggested to him by his colleague Beynon as the two men walked home through the blackout one evening. Beynon had, as part of his duties at Slough, been listening to the short-wave station broadcasting from Zeesen near Berlin. Observations showed certain inconsistencies in the ionosphere above this part of Germany—inconsistencies which Beynon noted above Slough half an hour later. At first Appleton was disbelieving. "What," he asked, "do you really think that I've been studying the ionosphere for more than 15 years and have missed that?" Nevertheless, he was soon convinced that the matter was worth investigation; almost as quickly he became convinced that the drift did in fact occur. Once this was so, Appleton turned in his customary way to an investigation of what the feature exactly was, how it occurred, what created it, and why.

The latter half of the 1940's also saw him investigating, with equipment developed as a direct result of war-time needs, a number of ionospheric problems which had been studied only more generally with the less effective pre-war instruments. Thus there came in the autumn of 1946 the chance of helping to elucidate a riddle that had intrigued him since his work in Norway 14 years previously. During his team's probing of the ionosphere its members had often observed transient echoes in the upper atmosphere. These echoes came from about 100 km up, lasted only a second or two, and were observed by day as well as by night. They came when frequencies high enough to pierce the ionosphere were used, and Appleton believed that they must come from dense concentrations of ionisation produced by meteor trails, although at the time there was no proof that this was the case. If it were, the fact would be interesting for two reasons. For due to the limitations of visual astronomy no one knew how many meteors were reaching the earth during the hours of daylight; in addition, conflicting evidence had prevented astronomers from forming any accurate estimate of the meteors' speed—data which would indicate whether all of them came from within the solar system. The next step came during the war when J. S. Hey and G. S. Stewart, working at the Army Operational Research Group during the V2 rocket bombardment of Britain, investigated a number of false alarms and concluded that what had been thought to be rocket echoes had in fact been produced by meteors. Further evidence was produced after the war when definite confirmation that the transient echoes were caused by meteors was obtained by J. S. Hey's team at AORG and afterwards by A. C. B. Lovell and his co-workers at Jodrell Bank. Striking evidence was provided by detailed correlations between the echoes and visual sightings of meteors.

Two months later, in October 1946, the Giacobinid shower, due on the 10th of the month, gave scientists the opportunity of a more decisive test, and Appleton organised one of a number of special teams which carried out observations on the nights of the 9th and the 10th. The results as observed by the various teams were conclusive, and Hey's team made the first radar measurements of the speed of the approaching meteors. "We had our apparatus working," Appleton later wrote of his own team's efforts, "and, at the time predicted, three in the morning, recorded thousands of transient echoes although before midnight there had been hardly any at all." The radar sightings were particularly useful since some of the visual ones were obscured by cloud. However, at places the reverse was the case. "We had a completely clear sky at Jodrell," says Sir Bernard Lovell. "It was such a vivid sight that I'll never forget it." There was also the case that was reported to Appleton personally. "In North Wales there happened to be a break in the cloud and some young ladies at a Girls' School, who had persuaded their Mistress to let them get up specially for the occasion, had an excellent view of the display and sent me a most interesting report on the subject," he later said. "What they saw must have been impressive indeed, for meteor streaks were appearing at the rate of two or three per second at the height of the shower."

One result of the night's observations from stations in many parts of Britain was, as Appleton later pointed out, that ionospheric soundings could provide "a reliable technique of meteor exploration which is applicable in all weathers and also during daylight. Moreover, since it is found that the effective reflecting power of meteor trails is increased as the exploring radio-frequency is reduced, we have been able to show that using pulses of lower radio-frequency, many meteor trails may be detected and examined which escape even telescope visual recognition."

The tracking of meteors with the help of radar was an early event in the history of the science that was to grow into radio astronomy. Another, and more important, development grew from remarkable events first reported by J. S. Hey. During February and March 1942, a number of radar stations round the British coast had reported strong radio noise on wavelengths of from 4 to 13 metres coming from the direction of the sun.

Hey, who investigated the phenomenon, circulated a report correlating the radio noise with solar activity associated with sunspots.

Hey's 1942 report had a very restricted circulation, and it was near the end of the war that Appleton first became aware of it when Hey described the occurrence at a meeting of the Ultra Short Wave Panel. Appleton then collaborated with Hey's team at AORG in further investigations. Then in 1946 another remarkable occurrence of radio emissions during sunspot activity provided the opportunity for a more detailed study of the phenomenon. Calculations showed that at times the radio flux was about 100,000 times as strong as would have been expected from the known temperature of visible stars. Appleton and Hey showed that there were unmistakable bursts of violent radio noise at the times of solar flares; and since it was known that such flares occurred in sunspot areas, while the radio noise disappeared as sunspot areas disappeared with the sun's rotation, it seemed clear that the two types of phenomena were correlated.

Later in the year, Appleton witnessed an interesting demonstration by Canadian workers showing that the radio noise originated in the sunspot region. By a lucky chance Appleton was able to watch the process. "The date was November 23rd, and I happened to be visiting the Canadian laboratory on that particular day," he said later. "There was a sunspot on the sun's face at the time, and, as the eclipse progressed, the sunspot region became obscured. And it was found that there was a marked decrease in solar noise when this happened."

This question of radio noise from the sun had a kinship with the older problem of galactic radio noise which was to become one of the main subjects for the inquiries of radio astronomy. This was a field in which Appleton was to be increasingly interested. "It seems to me," he wrote some years later to Professor, now Sir Bernard, Lovell, "that the new contribution that radio-astronomy is making to cosmological theory is a delightful example of something remote from social advancement. One really ought to want only truth to prevail; but I cannot help applauding anything which suggests that the continuous creation theory is wrong! I've always been faintly irritated by the arrogant way in which its sponsors lay down the law about it. What a pity we have not lived long enough to measure whether the average distance between galaxies has, or has not, altered with time. For that seems to me to be the essential difference between the two main cosmological theories."

Appleton himself had played his part in supporting the whole Jodrell Bank venture which had been Lovell's personal triumph. As Secretary of the DSIR he had backed the early work there before the major project had been put forward. Then, late in 1949, after he had left the Department, he came on the scene in a different role, being appointed to a committee of the Royal Astronomical Society set up to inquire into the whole future of radio astronomy in Britain. Lovell's was by far the most ambitious of the various schemes which had to be considered, and the vital meeting at which its fate was settled was held late in February 1950 in Appleton's rooms in the University of Edinburgh.

"After my explanation," Sir Bernard has written, "there were various questions, and then Appleton asked each member to state his final opinion on whether the Committee should back the proposal. I do not think that I have ever had such moments of suspense, as one by one the members gave their favourable opinions. Finally, Appleton said in words which I have never forgotten that he was 'impressed by the wide list of problems in astronomy and geophysics which Professor Lovell had listed as capable of solution by a radio-telescope of this size, but I am even more impressed by the possible uses of this instrument in fields of research that we cannot yet envisage'."

By this time Appleton had, despite his continuing wish to devote more time to research, untrammelled by administration, begun a university career that was to succeed those of scientist and of Whitehall administrator.

Early in this third career there occurred an incident that is best dealt with here, stretching back as it did through the immediate post-war years to the days of the pre-war defence effort. This was the hearing of the radar claim made by Watson-Watt and others to the Royal Commission on Awards to Inventors.

The patenting of inventions and of technological techniques which utilise the natural laws has for long been a subject of dispute among scientists. On the lower level there has been a difference of opinion as to the propriety of patenting ideas conceived in an employer's time; on a higher plane there has been argument about whether some techniques should be patented at all — a classic example being the differences between members of the French team on the question of patenting methods of producing an atomic bomb. In the case of awards to inventors of devices used specifically in war the position has, in practice, been looked at rather differently. In many cases the men concerned have been serving officers rather than scientists; claims have usually been made, moreover, on the grounds that those involved had gone beyond the line of duty; that they had worked harder, driven themselves further, than they might otherwise have done with the aim that fewer men should be left mangled on the battlefield. Their claims were, at the very least, rather special; that for radar was particularly so, since the method of detection not only had great post-war potential but had been initially developed, so it appeared, at roughly the same time in the United States, Germany, and Great Britain.

It was clear that Appleton would be called to give evidence before the Commission. His feelings about Watson-Watt were common knowledge, as were his views about the general subject of patents. "I hold that any scientific discovery does not belong, as of right, to its discoverer," he once said in a broadcast. "It belongs to mankind." Later, when working out with Lord Halsbury, the head of the Government National Research Development Corporation, how patents resulting from research work in Edinburgh University might best be dealt with, his views were made equally clear. "He took the view," says Lord Halsbury, "that any rewards should consist of promotion and additional pay — not royalties."

Appleton might, therefore, have been expected to appear as what, in another court, would have been called a hostile witness. This was to be far from the case. Naturally enough, he staked his own claim — not for a cash reward but for a place in history — when asked what contribution his ionospheric work had made to operational radar in 1935. "I think it must have been of great value in that you had automatically in your mind methods of range-finding, methods of finding radio ranges," he said. "You had your cathode ray oscillograph and you had your time bases. What was necessary of course was to get higher powers in the transmitter so as to be able to detect the smaller echoes that you get from an aircraft or a ship as compared with the echoes that you get from a large layer like the upper atmosphere."

That claim made, he was prepared to admit that it was primarily Watson-Watt and his team who had made operational radar possible in time for the Battle of Britain. There was a minor brush when Watson-Watt, cross-examining Appleton, raised the founder-membership of what he called the Radiolocation Club, and Appleton declared himself happy to be a member of an earlier group that included Faraday, Clerk Maxwell, and Hertz. But even on the surface Appleton gave genuine support to Watson-Watt's claim. In a private memorandum he prepared before the opening of the hearings, he went farther still. "But the biggest effort of all was being made by Watson-Watt, pleading, advocating, hustling, getting stores, masts, buildings," this went. "It was, above all, to his drive and powerful advocacy, that we had radar stations round our coast when war broke out. He has been good enough to acknowledge the value of my scientific radar, but practical radar, in the shape of stations that operated, was due much more to him than to anyone else. At the same time I am sure that it will be found that the actual *technical* turning of scientific radar into *aircraft detector radar* was due to Bowen and Wilkins. They did the real technical work at the bench and, of course, were joined by others. But here I must turn again to the supreme effort of Watson-Watt. He had the vision to see what it all implied. He just burned with it. It is true that he had the backing of the Tizard Committee but I am sure that it was Watson-Watt's leadership of the team and his powerful and eloquent advocacy that won the day with the Air Staff and the Treasury. Hence the country's operating radar stations in 1939."

This was a generous enough tribute from a man who felt as strongly as Appleton did about his own part in the birth of radar. It was even more so in the light of a letter which Appleton had written two months before the hearings began.

Early in February Sir Frank Smith, Appleton's predecessor at the DSIR, who was also to give evidence, had written asking Appleton for a copy of the Post Office report of 1932 which had called attention to the interruption of radio signals by aircraft. In his reply Appleton mentioned, also, the Bell investigation of 1933, and then went on: "But of course we must remember that, even before this, a complete patent for radar (both pulse and frequency-modulation) had been filed as a provisional in March,

1928." This was the secret Admiralty patent, a copy of which had been sent to Appleton in 1944, and Appleton now repeated to Smith the important opening paragraphs.

But there was no suggestion that either Watson-Watt or any of the other claimants involved had ever seen the Alder patent, so their ideas and work were genuinely independent and original. The birth of British operational radar therefore owed nothing to the stillbirth which had taken place 8 years previously.

The radar case hearings took place in the spring of 1951, two years after Appleton had moved from London to a new life north of the border. At the end of the war he had been 53. His initial five-year agreement with the Government had already been extended for a further five, but it is likely that his release would have been granted had he asked for it. However, the summer of 1945 had seen him deeply engaged in the Department's plans for expansion; he was not a man to leave a job half-done; and for the next three years he was engrossed in the plans that were being implemented as well as the tightened economy allowed. By the middle of 1948 the major part of this work, setting the Department firmly on the new rails laid down for it into the future, had been decently finished. Appleton had only some four more years to go before he reached the age of 60 and it was clear that the time had arived to move; if, that is, he wished to move at all.

In fact, he did wish to move, and for more reasons than one. He had never been partial to the ways of the Civil Service, and despite his considerable administrative skills he begrudged the hours during which these kept him from his beloved ionosphere. Here was one spur which was to drive him from the DSIR — the hope that he could return if not to a full-time scientific life at least to one where he could, for a major part of his time, direct scientific research. There was also the question of his wife, not particularly happy with London and of a nature which he felt might benefit from a complete change of environment. By the middle of 1948 Appleton was, therefore, as one colleague has put it, "looking round".

There is a continuing tradition among his family that during this period he had expectations of a Cambridge appointment, and more than one of his ionospheric colleagues has suggested that he still cast eyes on the Cavendish. This would have been not merely natural enough but almost inevitable. Sir Lawrence Bragg had by this time occupied the Cavendish chair for a decade; if he intended to move it seemed likely that he would do so before the 1950's, and it would have been almost superhuman of Appleton not to have nourished the hope of yet another return to the Cambridge where he had been so happy both a quarter of a century, and a decade, earlier. However, Sir Lawrence remained at the Cavendish – as he was to remain until his translation to the Royal Institution in 1953.

At this point it is perhaps necessary to stress the limitations imposed by the extent of Appleton's achievements. Like the editor of *The Times*, or the Foreign Secretary, he could take few steps that would not appear to be downhill. The Cavendish would, of course, be acceptable, as would a turn into the upper world of Whitehall where men such as Tizard, Cockcroft, Zuckerman, and Brundrett were already exercising – or at least trying to exercise – a new scientific power. Yet this world had never attracted Appleton; it was rather away from it, away into the field of pure research, that he now wished to move, and here there seemed a paucity of opportunities. But in the autumn of 1948, almost fortuitously, an opportunity arose.

The previous autumn he had been invited north, as Secretary of the DSIR, to the University of Edinburgh whose Principal and Vice-Chancellor, Sir John Fraser, had been setting up a University Industrial Liaison Committee. At the dinner and reception given in the University's upper library to inaugurate the Committee, Appleton gave the principal address, and more than one of the Curators of Patronage, who in their medieval way still exercised the City's ancient rights in the University's management, had been impressed both by his speech and his bearing.

Early in December 1947 Sir John unexpectedly collapsed and died on the library stairs of the Old College. There was some difficulty in replacing him, but 10 months later it became known in Edinburgh that Appleton might be available.

CHAPTER 10

1949–1959: PRINCIPAL AND VICE-CHANCELLOR

EARLY in October 1948 David, later Sir David, Milne, Permanent Under-Secretary of State for Scotland, wrote to the Lord Provost of Edinburgh, Sir Andrew Murray. Milne had already been consulted unofficially on the problem of finding a successor to Sir John Fraser as Principal and Vice-Chancellor, and he now heard that Appleton might be willing to move from London. He therefore consulted Sir Andrew, whose role in the University's affairs was far more than nominal.

Since the Edinburgh council had sought from Queen Mary in 1561 a grant of the ruins of Kirk-o'-Field on which to build a college, the city had played a dominating part in the University's affairs. Even though the Universities (Scotland) Act of 1858 had whittled down the city's powers, the Principal – as well as other academic staff – were still appointed by the Curators of Patronage, a body on which the City had four representatives against the University's three, and whose chairman was, *ex-officio*, the Lord Provost. Sir Andrew was now informed that Appleton was "not necessarily fixed in his present job and might consider an invitation for the headship of a university". To Edinburgh he would bring not only scientific eminence but the experience of a decade's administration in a testing war-time post, and his acquisition would be a bright feather in the City's cap.

Events now moved swiftly. Within nine days Sir Andrew had met Appleton and his wife in London and had formally suggested that he should come to Edinburgh as Principal and Vice-Chancellor; within three weeks Appleton and his wife had visited the city, toured the University, and been taken to Abden House, a splendid but deteriorating building overlooking Salisbury Crags that had recently been given to the University and was destined to become the Principal's official residence. All appeared to be going well, and Sir Andrew was shocked to receive, a few days later, a letter from Appleton which began: "After most careful consideration I have most regretfully reached the conclusion that I cannot accept the proposal you put to me last Monday."

Appleton had two reasons for turning down the appointment. One was that administration would, he felt, leave him little time for continuing his scientific work. "However, on this score I am not so sure that I would not be able to defeat circumstances, provided I could, in due course, build the small ionospheric observatory needed, with the funds I do not doubt I could get from various sources." More important was the impression which Abden House had created on Lady Appleton, an impression which her husband later explained to Sir Andrew and which he softened in a personal note. "To be effective one must have a happy and convenient background, the details of which run smoothly and with little attention," he wrote. "I was therefore quite taken aback when I saw the conditions and internal arrangements of the proposed Vice-Chancellor's house—in which, I gather, no previous Principal has lived. There is a family living in it at present in near-squalor conditions; and the only way in which it could be made suitable as one of the domestic centres of University life is for some thousands of pounds to be spent on its modernisation and decoration." He could, of course, lay down conditions of acceptance, but he did not wish to do so. It might have appeared that the matter was at an end.

However, the Lord Provost had by this time become seized of the idea. Refusing to take "no" for an answer, he now asked Appleton to reconsider his decision and to lay down the conditions under which he would accept the post. Appleton agreed. Only one more river then had to be crossed. He was still bound by his agreement with the Government, and it was necessary for him to ask Herbert Morrison for his release. The Lord President was somewhat reluctant since Sir Charles Darwin, Director of the National Physical Laboratory and in some ways Appleton's number two, was resigning in March; Sir Edward Mellanby, Secretary of the Medical Research Council, was also retiring while Sir John Fryer, Secretary of the Agricultural Research Council, had died only a few days previously. "So the Lord President is going to lose *all* his three principal officers about the same time," Appleton explained. However, the release was granted, and on 4 December the Lord Provost wrote confirming Appleton's appointment.

A few points still had to be settled. For one thing it was felt in Edinburgh that possibly Appleton himself, and certainly his wife, were going to Abden House reluctantly, only because there was no alternative. This was not so, Appleton wrote to the Secretary of the University. "There is, of course, no doubt that from the standpoint of our *private* life as citizens, my wife and I would wish for a smaller residence than Abden House. But, unless I am completely mistaken, it would be a positive contribution to the Society of the University if the Principal's house could be more than a private residence; and my wife and I are quite prepared to try to make Abden House serve in this connection. There we would hope to entertain the University staff and their wives as well as, say, officer representatives of undergraduate societies and organisations. There is also, I note, a fair 'turnover' of University staff each year and I would hope to be able to do something to make each newcomer feel welcome and so on; while there will certainly be visitors to be put up from time to time."

This promise was to be more than fulfilled, the result both of Appleton's welcoming personality and the unparalleled situation of Abden House itself. Built by Thomas Nelson the publisher soon after 1870, it was for almost half a century occupied by women members of the Nelson family as a form of dower house. In 1924 it had been sold by the Nelson Trustees to Lord Alness, the Lord Justice Clerk, who in turn disposed of it a decade later to Sir Donald Pollock. In 1946 Sir Donald had presented it to the University along with the rest of the Nelson Estate. An austere house of unknown Victorian parentage, built in the four-square Scottish way, it had certainly dropped downhill during the immediate post-war years. However, rehabilitation was not only possible but more than worth while in the light of the building's almost unique position. Lying on the south-east-

PLATE 17. Entering the McEwan Hall, Edinburgh, during the State Visit to Scotland of King Olav V of Norway, left; H.R.H. Prince Philip, Chancellor of the University, in background (*by courtesy of* Associated Newspapers).

PLATE 18A. (*above*) Sir Edward, second from left, about to open the Mullard Radio Astronomy Observatory, Cambridge, 1957 (*by courtesy of* A. C. K. Ware (Photographers) Ltd.).

PLATE 18B. (*below*) With Lord Adrian, right, and Professor P. M. S., later Lord, Blackett (*by courtesy of* A. C. K. Ware (Photographers) Ltd.).

PLATE 19.   Speaking in the URSI Commission on the Ionosphere at the XI URSI General Assembly, The Hague, 1954.

PLATE 20A. (*above*) The end of the Cowan House Race. The Principal congratulating the winner on the steps of the War Memorial, Old Quadrangle, University of Edinburgh (by courtesy of *The Scotsman*).

PLATE 20B. (*below*) Welcoming the President of India, Pandit Nehru, before his address to Students at Edinburgh University, 1961. Mrs. Pandit far right (*by courtesy of* George Outram & Co.).

ern fringe of the built-up area which skirts round Salisbury Crags, it had main rooms beyond which there stretched as a foreground the green acres of the Prestonfield Golf Course with, in the distance, a gleam of Dudding-ston Loch. To the left, helping to frame the scene, ran the line of Salisbury Crags with, more distantly, the outliers of Arthur's Seat. Appleton seized on the view—as did Sir William Hutchinson while working on the portrait of the Queen for the Merchant Company Hall in Edinburgh and still in doubt as to the best background to utilise. "I thought of Edinburgh Castle or Holyrood for that space, but obviously they were too important to go into that corner," he said later. "I decided on the view across Dud-dingston Loch and the Queen's Park one day when I was lunching with Sir Edward."

Appleton's letter describing how he wished to utilise Abden House gives a good idea of the spirit in which he moved north to pass what he described as the impermeable barrier between England and Scotland. He was not so much going as an Englishman to run a Scottish University; he was rather going as a scientist and administrator who from now onwards would become a part of the city of Edinburgh, as much a part of it as the deep trough in which the Nor Loch once lay, Calton Hill to the east with its glimpse of distant Berwick Law, or the crags at the west from whose castle one can see the line of the Highland hills.

Once the details were settled he began to wind up his affairs in the DSIR. He told his Private Secretary that he would "see him in the clear"; thus ensuring that the official did not have the task of training a suc-cessor. He prepared his farewells, apparently overjoyed to be cutting the painter which linked him to both London and Whitehall, holding a stir-rup-cup party at the Athenaeum and a "leaving party" at the DSIR which was long remembered for his parodied version of the Civil Service Esta-code.

Then, in April, he arrived in Edinburgh, finding the renovation at Abden House still in progress and being forced to stay in an hotel for a number of weeks. The situation had one advantage, for the grounds were being laid out by the Royal Botanic Gardens and, arriving while work was still in progress, Appleton had the chance of explaining exactly what he wanted, asking for a rose-bed round which the approach drives were to

Sir Edward Appleton

curl, and ensuring that the other beds were filled with wall-flowers, daffo-
dils, and dahlias, all of his favourite yellow. He spent a good deal of his
own money on the gardens, took a deep personal interest in them, and in
1958 wrote of how he had "had much enjoyment out of exchanging plants
with other people in the University who are also gardeners".

He formally took up his post as Principal of the University of Edinburgh in May 1949. His hopes were high, his expectations great, and for
more than one reason. First there was, as he had already appreciated
through his membership of the University Grants Committee, scope for a
genuine revival in the University. Its great days had been during the final
decades of the previous century when Edinburgh's reputation for medicine
and the law had spread the University's fame around the world. Since
then there had been a gradual but persistent decline. During the years
immediately before the war it had tended to rest in the doldrums, academic sails hanging limply from the masts, a result partly of over-satisfac-
tion with its great past and partly of the city's reluctance to move with the
times.

This traditional feeling that what had been good enough for the previous generation was good enough for the present had been curiously
strengthened by the war. Compared with some of the other great university cities — Glasgow and Liverpool, Manchester and London — Edinburgh
had been untouched by the real hardships; and while much of Britain and
much of Scotland was looking forward eagerly to the new world that
could be built for the second half of the twentieth century, a fair percentage
of Edinburgh tended to look back nostalgically and hope for a reconstruction of the world that had ended on 3 September 1939. This feeling was
not, of course, universal. But it ran as a persistent current through much
of the city's affairs and it was not to make Appleton's task any easier.
A conservative with a small *c* by nature and a large *C* by conviction, he
yet realised that if the University was to play its full part in the future, then
great changes were inevitable during the next two decades. The physical
expansion of the University, necessary already but essential before its
student population was to double, as expected, was the most explosive
factor in such changes. But there were to be other factors involving the
constitution of the University, and the curriculum, as well as details which

164

had been lovingly added to its traditions during three and a half centuries.

Bringing about these changes while preserving the essentials, raising the University to its previous position—this was what Appleton saw as his task, a great opportunity which he now enthusiastically pepared to seize. The challenge involved was, indeed, one of the things which had attracted him during his talks in London with the Lord Provost. Another, although more than one of his friends thought the fact curious, was the attraction of Scotland itself. There is sometimes claimed to be an affinity between the Scot and the Yorkshireman that does not exist between the Scots and the rest of the English; and it is certainly true that Appleton's birth south of the Border was only rarely held against him in any of the disputes which inevitably arise when gown faces town; even then, the fact was often pointed out only in lieu of any other argument. Yet Appleton's love of Scotland and the Scots, a love that rose from deep down and was not assumed for the sake of convenience, stemmed very largely from the strong contrast between his practical Yorkshire background and the romantic appeal of the country that owes more to the Young Pretender and the Scottish Tourist Board than it does to the facts of life. He was a great man for Charlie-over-the-waterism. He had soaked in Scott as a youth, and he retained for the whole of his life the romantic schoolboy image of Mary Queen of Scots as a beautiful tragic queen. For Appleton there were few corners of Edinburgh in which there could not be seen, at least with the eye of faith, the faint shadow of a figure, whether historic or fictitious mattered little, from a richer, rougher, and more colourful age. This attraction of Edinburgh, the city which any perceptive Englishman must regard as one of the great foreign capitals of the world, had been felt on his first visit, and he had written to an acquaintance of how he counted it "with its magic and romance, an ideal setting for a University".

Thus he began, and cultivated with an almost passionate intensity to the end of his life, an interest in the topography and history of Edinburgh itself. And it was typical that he should write with immense delight to Wilfrid Taylor, a friend of *The Scotsman*, inquiring whether he knew "that Walter Scott used the word 'detergent', when a traveller is anxious to use such a substance to remove the Rizzio bloodstains in Holyroodhouse, with its present meaning". This spirit of almost schoolboyish enthusiasm never left him, and it provided some compensation for one grievous miscalculation he had made when accepting the Edinburgh appointment. This miscalculation, implicit in much of his correspondence over the years, was spelt out in two letters which were typical of many. Declining the chairmanship of the Royal Society's Sectional Committee for Physics five months after going to Edinburgh he regretfully noted: "I am finding the burden here much heavier than I expected." And, two and a half years later, turning down the offer of the chairmanship of the Radio Research Board — "the most attractive of all the DSIR jobs I could ever hope to be asked to do" — he explained that he had "completely misjudged the amount of work that has to be done here in Edinburgh".

Had this limitation, imposed by the mass of administration involved in doubling the University's size, affected merely his marginal interests, the position would have been different. In practice it prevented even the starting of an ambitious scheme which he had been considering even before the end of the war. Early in 1945 Appleton had mentioned to some of his colleagues a proposal to set up, when peace came, a Radio Research Institute which would incorporate the Radio Division of the National Physical Laboratory. It is not clear whether he envisaged running the Institute himself or merely organising it from his position as Secretary of the DSIR, and then keeping a close hand on its growth. What is clear is that he implanted in the minds of at least some Slough workers the idea of a major post-war expansion. The success of the idea was now to rebound on him.

For now that he was leaving the DSIR for Edinburgh the idea became transformed into that of a major postgraduate research group inside the University which would deal with "Solar and terrestrial relationships". This scheme was discussed by Appleton with Piggott, with Beynon, and with a number of other fellow-workers before he left London, and it was suggested to a number of them that they should take up appointments under him in Edinburgh. All refused, not least because none of them expected Appleton to remain in Edinburgh for more than a few years. Added to this was the belief, particularly among those in government service, that Slough itself might expand to include just such a body — along the lines of Appleton's proposed Radio Research Institute.

His plans for the proposed Edinburgh research group were outlined in a memorandum which he drew up shortly before he left London. The work of the "Solar and terrestrial relationships" group would, he explained, supplement that already being carried out in Scotland on the relations between solar and terrestrial phenomena. There would, he added, be an excellent opportunity for linking together observations such as (a) solar phenomena which were already being studied at the Edinburgh Observatory, (b) auroral phenomena, already being studied in the Department of Natural Philosophy, (c) magnetic phenomena which were being recorded at Eskdalemuir and Lerwick Stations under the control of the Meteorological Office in Edinburgh, and, of course, (d) radio studies phenomena in the upper atmosphere. Much important work could be done by reducing and correlating data from all four kinds of observations, and "a theoretical group attacking such problems would be ideally situated at Edinburgh University because of the strong Mathematical Laboratory already existing there. If it is possible, as I hope, to exchange ionospheric results obtained in Edinburgh (Lat. 56°N) with those obtained by other Stations in other parts of the World," Appleton went on, "we could build up a small theoretical team engaged on elucidating ionospheric and other phenomena from a world viewpoint. I need only mention the subject of solar and lunar tides in the ionosphere and the world morphology of ionospheric storms to indicate the kind of problems before us."

It would, he explained, be necessary to set up a field station, preferably about half a mile from occupied premises, but there seemed to be no apparent difficulty about this, especially as an unused war-time radar or radio station would be ideal. There would have to be accommodation for the theoretical workers, but the whole scheme had already been discussed with Dr. Smith-Rose of the Radio Research Station at Slough, who was "already tentatively earmarking equipment for possible use". This was an imaginative project and one which Appleton was peculiarly equipped to direct. The formation of such a "school" would, moreover, have enabled him to do for Edinburgh something of what J. J. Thomson and Rutherford had done for Cambridge at the Cavendish and Lindemann had done for Oxford at the Clarendon.

What in fact happened was very different. Appleton did carry on with his own private ionospheric researches while grappling with University administration—there were, from time to time, critical comments that he devoted undue time to them. But they were to be of a totally different order, and on an entirely different scale, from those he had envisaged. Indeed, in the climate of the times, anything else would have been surprising; for the days had gone for ever when it was possible for the head of a University to devote his time to research and dismiss administration during the casual odd half-hour. It is quite clear that Appleton had failed to appreciate that this change had taken place between the comparatively leisurely days of a pre-war Cambridge and those of the University industry a decade later. There may well have been an unexpected reason for this attitude, so comparable to that of Sir Henry Tizard who had gone to Magdalen in 1943 with the memory of his predecessor at Imperial College in mind, the Sir Thomas Holland who used to claim that he had reduced the running of Imperial College to 20 minutes a day. It is not clear how well Appleton knew Holland; but the latter had been Sir John Fraser's predecessor at Edinburgh for 15 years.

Appleton did not complain about these burdens which effectively robbed him of what might have been a scientific cornerstone to his career. He was not the complaining sort, and it was with unqualified hopes for the future that on 1 May he formally took office as Principal, the Curators of Patronage having appointed him "until the end of the academical year in which he shall have completed the seventy-fifth year of his age".

As was the custom, there was no public installation, but on the 11th Appleton presented his Commission from the Curators to a meeting of the Senatus, the governing body of the University, and took his seat as chairman on the invitation of the Senior Professor. Five days later he was himself appointed by the University Court as a Curator of Patronage; and, a shadow of the work to come, he now became a Trustee of the Carnegie Trust for the Universities of Scotland, a member of the Association of Universities of the British Commonwealth, and also a member of six separate standing committees of the Court covering subjects as diverse as student health, finance, business and law, and post-war development. This was not all. The business of running the University involved a total of about 70 standing committees, as well as between 70 and 100 *ad hoc* committees. At all of these Appleton now had the right to take the chair. And while there are limits to human endurance, it is nevertheless true that a working knowledge of what was happening in many of them was essential to any Principal hoping to run the University on a more than touch-and-pass basis.

During the first few months that followed his induction, Appleton dined out four or five nights a week, usually accompanied by his wife. Although naturally a sociable man, this programme was part of a deliberate policy of making himself known, of "breaking the ice". So was the extraordinarily thorough briefing which he had given himself. His life-long enthusiasm for Sir Walter Scott helped; so did his admiration for the line of Scots scientists which stretched back past Ramsay and Dewar to Clerk Maxwell and Simpson. But on this firm foundation he had built a knowledge of the more specialist aspects of Scottish history that surprised his listeners. His attention to detail was impressive. Well in advance, secretaries or staff would be asked to check all that was checkable; and while city elders would discover an English Principal apparently at ease with their history, businessmen would find him well acquainted with the story of Edinburgh's trade, and doctors express surprise at his knowledge of Scotland's early medical history.

His enthusiasm was not simulated. "I assure you that I am proud to be Principal of the University, and a citizen of the capital of Scotland," he said at a dinner a few months after taking up his appointment, "and I cannot express my own feelings better than by quoting to you: 'The city, with its traditions and history, its monuments and public buildings, the Castle surmounting a precipitous rock, the church of the Holy Rood with its royal palace, the ancient streets and modern squares associated with nobles, divines, philosophers, men of letters and of science, took firm possession of my imagination.' No one with a feeling for the past but must become inspired by such an environment, and be impelled to labour for his generation and for the future."

Within a short while Appleton was making himself noticed, as a matter of policy, and in his own individual way. "I find it quite impossible to be 'self-effacing' in Edinburgh," he once wrote, "but I take the greatest possible care in the preparation of everything I say at any function, Town or Gown, knowing that I cannot dissociate myself from my office. This involves hours of preparation and even the weighing of phrases (which, I hope, are not evident in the final result) but I think such consideration to be essential." It was not only essential but was properly noted. "It was clear," says one of his professors who watched him, at first critically, during these early weeks, "that Scotland suited him." Another thing was soon clear: after due deliberation the body of the kirk decided that he suited Scotland.

The very genuine affection that Appleton felt, and showed, for Scotland and the Scots, helped during the first months of his appointment to improve the strategic position from which he could fight the battles that lay ahead. So did his attitude to another matter which might have raised a problem. As Principal and Vice-chancellor he held a position in the city of Edinburgh second only to that of the Lord Provost; and while it would have been difficult for the effective head of any university to have avoided taking some religious stance, in Edinburgh this would have been impossible.

What might have been an embarrassing situation was avoided by the stage to which Appleton's beliefs had evolved. His upbringing had been of the strictly Methodist sort which is now of interest mainly to historians and sociologists; Sunday school, choir-singing, and regular attendance had been only some of the items in an attitude which, as he grew older, appeared to have less link with the rest of the world outside Bradford. This was the result of many things—the natural swing of the pendulum, the secular scientific society in which he moved, the demands of more pressing things to occupy his thoughts. Yet Appleton's reactions over the years had been more complex than the familiar ones. It is true that he had, as one of his former school-fellows said with resignation, "tended to fall away". Yet as a later colleague put it, "he was one of those scientists who continued to remain a Christian". Furthermore, during the years that followed the war, he appeared to be falling back. If he was not an enthusiastic churchman, his fundamental beliefs yet allowed him to remain in the fold without any pangs of conscience. And now that he had arrived in Edinburgh he was able to take his place in the Canongate kirk for the Easter celebrations, for the Christmas carols, and for the occasional service, with feelings totally different from those of the elderly taking out religious insurance.

These feelings were in line with his view of the limitations of science. "It has nothing to say about the affairs of the human heart — nothing to say about love, affection, repentance, forgiveness — issues of admittedly greater moment than even science itself," he said during one BBC broadcast to Europe. Conversely, he reminded the members of the Anglo-Swedish Society in one address that "we must never forget that science enlarges men's minds and can bring home to everyone the wonders and significance of the world in which we live". And to a correspondent who wrote to him about what he termed the religious side of the satellite experiments, he wrote: "I think that there are scientists sufficiently humble to realise that, as they disclose the wonders of nature's secrets, they are dealing with things which have been wonderful all the time — since their creation." The sense of wonder, and of mystery, remained with him, providing a stout support for his general religious beliefs and helping to provide a genuine atmosphere of dedication to the work to which he now turned.

For the next decade and more, Appleton's main task was that of coping with the great expansion of the University which was thrust upon it by outside pressures, an expansion which involved almost a doubling of students, a great increase in staff, and an extension of the University precincts that was to split Edinburgh into two bitterly opposed camps. This work was to be superimposed upon that of the normal University administration. It was, moreover, made more complicated than it would have been before the war by the increased pressures which the Government were now exercising in the field of education. Edinburgh, like all other universities, was finding the role of the University Grants Committee to be of ever-growing significance, and from May 1949 onwards Appleton was to be engaged in a long and complicated series of discussions with the UGC chairman, Sir Keith Murray, later Lord Newhaven. These discussions always appear to have been amiable; but their complexity, the convolutions of the brief to which Appleton had to speak or write, and the inroads that this work alone made on his time were of formidable proportions. In addition, what would even in England have been a massive task of administrative reconstruction was made more complex by the fact that

English decisions often had to be, as it were, translated for implementation north of the Border by the Scottish Education Department. If any further complication was required it could easily be found in the existence of the Secretary of State for Scotland whose aid might – in controversial matters such as the George Square expansion was to become – be invoked by either party to an argument.

Steering the University ship through these troubled post-war years was more than a full-time job; so much so that University officers more than once suggested that Appleton should appoint a deputy to help him in the more routine administrative work. He always refused, preferring, instead, to draw heavily on the experience of the University Secretary, Charles Stewart. Although heads were sometimes shaken at this method, the system worked; whatever else can be questioned, there is no doubt that the University emerged from Appleton's principalship with raised standards, better prospects, and characteristics more attuned to the twentieth century than they had been in 1949.

This was the more surprising in that here, as at the DSIR during the war, Appleton managed to engage in a huge volume of extra-curricular work. He remained a member of the BBC's Engineering Advisory Committee; he served on the Radio Research Board until pressure of University work at last forced him off. He maintained, as part of his own office, and paid for out of Royal Society or similar grants, one or more workers and assistants devoted to his ionospheric work.

And within a few months of moving to Edinburgh he had been co-opted on to the first of numerous bodies run from St. Andrews House in the interests of Scotland or from the City Chambers in the interests of Edinburgh. This was the new Advisory Committee on Medical Research of which he became chairman. It was a new field for him, but it was one in which he had for long been interested and one to which he believed physics could make a contribution. The distinguished team which comprised the Committee was quickly stimulated by his views on research, illustrated by examples from his own subject, and it was equally soon clear that he was a good chairman. He had three main aims for the Committee. One was the establishment in Soctland of research units which would not be merely "out-stations" but centres of specialist work which would attract workers unhampered by routine hospital or professional duties. Second was the maintenance of adequate financial support for research in universities and hospitals. Thirdly, he believed that young research workers should be stimulated to look to the Committee for encouragement and for friendly interest in their work and future prospects.

The work was attractive but it was also arduous and in the autumn of 1954, after guiding the Committee through its first 4 years of life, Appleton was forced to retire by pressure of other work. But by that time he was further committed on behalf of the Scottish authorities. "I have a good deal on my plate from St. Andrews House here, at the moment," he wrote to the Secretary of the Royal Society when asked to write an obituary memoir of a former colleague, "(a) supply of Science and Maths teachers, (b) Peat Utilisation, (c) Civil Defence, and for the last four years I've been chairman of the Advisory Committee on Medical Research (Scotland) as Himsworth knows, and I cannot get free till a certain stage is reached in each case."

All this was organised from the big airy first-floor room in the Old College, facing the portraits of David Hume and of Robert Rollock, the first Principal. Appleton believed that habit oiled the machinery of administration as much as the mechanics of one's own private life, and at 9.45 on most week-day mornings he would mount the University staircase, stopping to pass a word of congratulation or consolation to the staff about the fortunes of Hibernians or Heart of Midlothian.

He would start the day by going through his mail, ringing for his secretary, and then dealing with the bulk of the letters. At 10.30 he usually saw his research assistant, Mrs. Turnbull — who later became Mrs. Pritchard — and discussed ionospheric work with her. At 10.45–11.00 the Secretary of the University, Charles Stewart, arrived, and for about an hour they would discuss various University problems. Each day would thereafter follow its own pattern. There might well be visitors about noon, while on at least two or three days a week there would be an official luncheon at which Appleton would have to speak. The afternoon would often be filled with committee work. There was also the work of the University Court which met once a month, and was mainly concerned with appointments and with finance — even though there existed a separate Finance

Committee on which Appleton sat. Decisions were rarely put to the vote; more usually, the chairman would wind up, rhetorically asking whether such and such was in fact the feeling of the meeting, and in this Appleton's DSIR experience came to his aid. And the day might end by an official reception or by a return to Abden House with the prospect of semi-official conversations with staff or visiting professors. More rarely, there would be a quiet evening occupied with Trollope, Plato, or the newest scientific books and papers; with "escape into the upper atmosphere"; or with the drafting of yet another of the speeches required of him at official functions.

Appleton was provided by the University with a private secretary and an assistant secretary on whom there devolved the typing of his ionospheric papers with their mass of technicalities unusual in normal secretarial work. It was typical of Appleton that the young woman faced with them was presented, on the first morning of her new work, with a carefully typed sheet of paper. "You will probably find these useful," said the Principal as he handed her a list of all the technical phrases she might be expected to meet.

In 1952 there came to work for him a new private secretary, Mrs. Helen Allison, the widowed daughter of the late John Gordon Lennie, a well-known Edinburgh business man, and Mrs. Margaret Lennie of Merchiston Park, Edinburgh. A tall, good-looking young woman, a former officer in the Women's Royal Naval Service, always on top of things and totally unflappable, she had been working for a few years in the University where her organising ability had quickly been recognised. This was to be ideally used in her new post, where she soon became essential to the efficient running of Appleton's abnormally busy life. Throughout the following years she became, in fact, a support without whose aid he might well have been crushed by the heavy burden of work.

Appleton enjoyed speaking at the dinners where he was now so often a guest of honour, just as he enjoyed the good food and wine, the formal ceremonies, the immaculate clothes, the sense of being, metaphorically as well as literally, placed at the top table. Some of his colleagues said he enjoyed it too much; but even the more critical were forced to admit that his casual professionalism when it came to the set-piece speech often helped to swing opinion the way that the University wished. He was extraordinarily good at all this, partly because he enjoyed big occasions, but even more because he had acquired over the years the physical and mental techniques to provide, without fail, a first-class finished performance. Thus on one famous occasion the transmitting microphone went dead when he was half-way through a speech. Appleton, hearing the slight click and realising what had happened, raised his voice without a moment's hesitation, or a break in his sentence, putting it so deftly across the room that only those nearest to him knew of the technical hitch.

Content counted as well as delivery. "I happen to be one of those people who *must* put a lot of preparation into any speech I make," he wrote to a friend, "so that far more is involved than the actual delivery." This had been true even before his Edinburgh days. Now, when the after-dinner speech was more frequently turned from a series of social pleasantries into a useful instrument for getting things done, he kept a series of folders and files marked "Material for speeches" into which went whatever he felt might be grist for his post-prandial mill. It was a curious but useful mixture. Giles cartoons and *Times* leaders went into it; so did notes of the numbers of University graduates; excerpts from *Science and the Poet*, and from Eliot's *The Cocktail Party*; funny stories—reported, read, or heard; and odd thoughts of his own such as "the odour of academic sanctity is a strong perfume and a little bit of it goes a long way".

This general background material would be supplemented when necessary by brief queries sent out to the University staff or to friends, asking for details of a story or a quotation which would be particularly apt for the speech being prepared, and which he now wished to check. His first long-hand draft would be typed and corrected, and the final version usually typed on a thick stack of sheets, each perhaps taking only 150 words, and many broken up by capitalised words such as SCIENTIFIC STORY, PROFESSOR STORY, or CAMBRIDGE STORY. "And," he commented to one colleague, "I usually go on polishing (and picking up things *during* the dinner!) up to the time of delivery."

Appleton would invariably start with a story. It was usually a good one, and it would, so to speak, put his listeners off their guard. He would then start reading, but would successfully avoid letting this be seen. "In giving lectures and addresses and making speeches I have found it useful to have my notes typed in what is called 'Great Primer' type (see attached)," he wrote to the University's Secretary soon after his arrival in Edinburgh. "This can easily be seen at a distance." Thus equipped, he was able to give the impression to at least a majority of those present that he was virtually speaking impromptu. If they began to doubt it there would come, as often as not, Appleton's sudden raising of the head, a look round the room and a comment, apparently on the spur of the moment and beautifully timed, such as: "Now, I remember an old character of my student days in Cambridge" — a polished example of art concealing art. He spoke French badly, with an accent he did little to correct — possibly because he had heard it said that he spoke it like Winston Churchill — and another of his mannerisms was to pause, look about him, and then repeat, slowly and emphasising every word, what he considered to be some particularly important passage. Many of those who watched him carefully over the years believed that these repetitions were typed into his draft. This was not so; but the words were underlined.

There was a strongly individual style in the stories he told. These were always of the proper kind, frequently had a scientific or at least an academic background, and were carefully selected for each particular audience. Thus he would tell scientists how a visitor to Harwell had signed the book with two X's. "He was asked what they meant," Appleton would go on, "and he then explained that the first was his signature as he was unable to write. Then they asked him what the second one was for. 'Oh,' he explained, 'that's my Ph.D.' " When it came to lecturing in out-of-the-way places, or to non-scientific audiences, he would sometimes ask if those at the back of the hall could hear him — and then explain that he had been nervous about the reply. "There was the time," he would go on, "when another lecturer asked that and a man at the back of the hall shouted out 'No.' He was immediately answered by a man in the front row who looked back and said: 'I'll change places with you: so far I've heard every word.' "

He enjoyed telling his own personal stories and would recount with delight how he and various colleagues at one period travelled down to

London for meetings of Principals and Vice-Chancellors. He would then explain how when he was visiting one of the Vice-Chancellors' homes, his colleague's wife had explained how much her husband enjoyed visiting London for the fortnightly meetings. "And such is the solidarity of Vice-Chancellors," Appleton would add, "that no-one ever told her that the Vice-Chancellors met only once a month."

At this level, as at the level of staff and students, Appleton's solid amiability helped him to deal with the major and continuing controversy into which he had been pitchforked on arrival in Edinburgh. This was "the George Square argument", and the handling of it was to be the thing above all others for which the University was to remember him.

He helped to reorganise its finances, bringing to this subject his own investment experience and ensuring that its funds were used to the best advantage. He brought in some notable men, such as Michael Swann, his successor as Principal, who was to transform biological teaching in the University from museum classification to experimental work, and Tom Cottrell, later to become first Principal of the new Stirling University. He encouraged an informal interplay of thought and ideas between the medical, the arts, and the science faculties at various levels, and by supporting Common Market studies, the extension of computer studies, and the use of a Scottish Universities nuclear reactor, helped to keep Edinburgh level with the newer universities.

All this provides evidence of Appleton's work as Principal. The George Square controversy stretched not only his administrative skill but also his experience of human nature. It was a controversy in which he was to be deeply involved for most of his remaining years, and it epitomised, in one single, central argument, most of the problems involved in the University's expansion. The extent of this expansion is illustrated by four simple figures: during the two decades which followed the University's last normal pre-war year, the number of students rose from 3716 to 7004 and the number of full-time staff from 185 to 612, although at the end of the decade the University occupied, so far as teaching was concerned, substantially the same accommodation as at the beginning. "The present shortage of class room, tutorial room, laboratory, examination room, and office accommodation imposes a severe strain on all members of the

University," noted a report by the University's Development Committee in the year that Appleton arrived as Principal. "If the University has gained rather than lost ground during the past five years, it is due to the efforts of its staff. But the efforts cannot continue, and the strain cannot be imposed, indefinitely."

The difficulty of accommodating a university that was persistently outgrowing its clothes was not merely a post-war problem. Since its foundation in the heart of the Old Town, its links with the rest of Edinburgh had grown progressively stronger, and these militated against the obvious solution of moving to a site outside the city. Students lived in lodgings rather than halls of residence, and had built up over the centuries a tradition very different from that which regarded "town" and "gown" as two separate entities. They used the National and City Libraries as well as their own, justly claimed to be "one of the most beautiful library halls in Europe". They were "of" the city in a way that was not entirely accounted for by the traditions of Scottish education or the fact that a fair percentage of students came from Edinburgh itself and another sizeable proportion from the hinterland. Even so, despite the resulting natural reluctance to move from the city centre site, the University had even before the First World War bought for development a plot of land a mile and a half to the south of the University, on the outskirts of the city and at the foot of the Braid Hills. Here there came in 1921, to what were known collectively as the King's Buildings, the Departments of Chemistry, Zoology, Animal Genetics, Geology, and Engineering—refugees from a city whose flourishing central area could no longer cope with the demands of its university for fresh accommodation. This radical move was, according to taste, either a major error or a great opportunity which was badly fumbled. For it was true, as the *University of Edinburgh Journal* was to put it, that "the original King's Buildings move might well have been the first step to the building of a *cité universitaire* on the Liberton–Blackford ridge, or the line of development favoured by Sir Frank Mears of a spread eastward from the Old College down to the Pleasance slope might have offered a splendid opportunity for massive reconstruction". It is not clear whether Sir Thomas Holland, Principal and Vice-Chancellor from 1929 until 1944, disapproved of the move, or whether his courage failed him; it is quite clear that during the decade before the war a great chance was lost. No move was made towards either a *cité universitaire*, or Mears's scheme for a "Collegiate Mile" parallel to the Royal Mile in the Old Town. As the pressure on space increased during the 1930's the University was thus left, bursting at its central seams, with a set of separate out-stations for which no development plans had been made.

As a substitute there was evolved in 1938 and 1939 what came to be known as the Master Plan, a scheme for the expansion and development of the University in and around its central site and involving, as a first step, an extension to the existing Medical Buildings on the north side of George Square. The war, and the aftermath of the war, effectively intervened. Only in February 1949, a mere three months before Appleton's arrival in Edinburgh, did the Town Council approve this first step in the Master Plan. To many in Edinburgh it had the effect of a shot across the bows, a warning that the enemy were in earnest. For it was feared, and with good reason, that University action on one side of George Square would merely be the prelude to the Square's gradual transformation into a purely University area as outlined in the Master Plan.

The bitterly contested struggle for which both sides now began to limber up their heavy artillery was to be in many ways a classic example of the argument between the conservationists and the innovators; in a Britain still struggling into the modern world, it has overtones of interest outside Edinburgh. However, the relatively simple problem of whether or not George Square should be preserved was complicated by the problem of the University's place in the city's life. This larger issue enclosed the smaller and purely architectural one, so that while the most heated arguments might rage over the disputed merits of George Square, an impression was sometimes given that this was merely the ground on which the battle was being fought, and was not, necessarily, the main issue at all.

The University's unique position as the 400-year-old child of the Edinburgh municipal authorities was a big factor. As the dispute grew, art, in the form of the conservationists, was claimed in some imaginations to be shaping up against science, in the form of Appleton. The capital value of the ground involved was one point not to be ignored; another was the long-term traffic problem of the city, while throughout the 1950's a multiplicity of vested interests tended to enter the conflict, hand on heart, and swearing that they were doing so for only the most worthy and objective of motives. Reading the thick stack of documents, newspaper cuttings, and impassioned pleas that the George Square controversy produced, it is difficult not to feel that it might form the heart of a great modern novel; or, perhaps, of a film made in lighter vein.

Studying the diametrically contrasting views of those who fought for and against the University invasion and the destruction of George Square, it appears that its architectural merits must have lain very much in the eye of the beholder. Erected by a private builder in the eighteenth century a few hundred yards to the south-west of the Old College, it comprised a simple rectangle of sober houses enclosing quiet gardens. Compared with the mishmash of many later buildings and streets, it was not merely inoffensive but pleasing to the eye, although the same can be said of more buildings in Edinburgh than in most other British cities. Whether greater claims should be made is a moot point, but it is perhaps significant that Murray in his 1894 *Handbook to Scotland*, a volume which generously lavishes "magnificent" and "handsome" on other Edinburgh sites, merely uses of George Square the single adjective "old-fashioned". The houses had once been the homes of the middling merchant classes and Sir Walter Scott's father, a Writer to the Signet, had lived at Number 25 – a fact sometimes tempting the square's defenders to confuse their generations and describe the house as the birthplace of Sir Walter himself. Since Scott's days, the area had tended to go downhill, a deterioration increased, as the twentieth century limped on, by the difficulties of finding enough servants. It is true that some of the buildings continued to be used as private houses, but an increasing number were occupied by more than one family. The decline continued and the word "slum" began to be used. Whatever the architectural merits for which the square had been noted – and it is difficult to deny that they existed – these had become increasingly covered by the ravages of neglect. A few homes still retained their old character and their dignity; quite as many, it was pointed out, retained dry rot.

Edinburgh Town Council's agreement to expansion of the University

Medical Buildings on the north side of George Square, given only a few months before Appleton's arrival, had certain qualifying clauses. In effect these relegated to limbo the other proposals in the Master Plan involving George Square and threw on to the University the onus of investigating, once again, any possible alternatives. More specifically, they threw this task on to Appleton who as Convener of the now re-constituted Development Committee would inevitably be the target for attack whichever way the final argument went.

His own personal position was made easier by the fact that he was new to the problem. He had no preconceived ideas. No one could really claim that he was *parti pris*. Thus his position now was somewhat similar to the one he had occupied during the war when, for instance, the Meteorological Office and Bomber Command, or the Ministry of Labour and the Air Ministry, had agreed to abide by the decision of such an honest broker. Against this, he had two handicaps. He was a scientist, and it was undeniable that the demands for more university space were aggravated by the expansion of science teaching which formed an impor-tant part of the University's plans. Secondly, he was not a Scot, a limita-tion which was rarely used as a weapon against him. However, it was a weapon always ready to hand and in the years-long controversy that lay ahead any weapon was sometimes better than none. "Englishman Go Home", scrawled on the walls of the Old College, failed to worry him, but it showed that the argument had widened out to include the rabble, and it did disturb his wife.

During 1949 five separate sub-committees of the Development Committee worked hard at evaluating alternatives to the George Square plan. It is probably unfair to the University to suggest that this work was less partial than it would have been had Appleton not recently become Principal; yet it is nevertheless true that each of the alternatives was considered in most convincing detail. The most obvious alternative was the steady transfer of the entire University to the King's Buildings site. This was rejected, as Appleton explained to the Town Council's Planning Committee, on grounds of cost, and also because the University would become divorced from the Medical School which had to remain in the city, close to the Royal Infirmary. But the nub of the matter lay elsewhere;

for such a move would result in "the eventual abandonment of the Old College and the subsequent further isolation from the Town, involving not only a break with tradition but also the loss of a magnificent and historic building". Two other alternatives, development either south or east of the existing university, were ruled out by the lie of the land, by other plans for city development or by their failure to provide the University with the essentials of a central quadrangle and interior lines of communication. A fourth possibility, dual development both at the King's Buildings and in the central area, would involve making the worst of both worlds.

There remained the major use of George Square, and it was this which Appleton described to the Town Council in 1950 as providing "by far the greatest advantages of coherence and compactness, and at the same time ... the practical possibility of bringing University development to fruition within a reasonable time". The Square would be transformed "wholly into an academic quadrangle, with the possibility in the more distant future of linking that quadrangle with the Old College, itself a quadrangle, by way of further university precincts". The houses on one side might be preserved — or at least their façades might be preserved; although when it came to using them for university accommodation, an examiner found "evidence of roofs, windows, doors, floors and fabric at many points being unsatisfactory and certainly requiring extra expenditure if departments were to be housed there". He pointed out the great difficulties of new wiring for electricity, the lack of sufficient natural lighting for academic work in many of the rooms — involving either refenestration or artificial light, or both; the difficulties with drainage involved in putting in a sufficient number of lavatories; and the presence of woodworm in the floors as well as wet rot. However. the gardens would certainly remain, and so would public access to them. But a library, almost inevitably of massive appearance, would fill the south-western corner of the square; laboratories and teaching blocks would rise to the east, and there was a suspicion, fully justified, that these would include tall towers. For all practical purposes, however carefully some façades were retained as semi-museum pieces, George Square would cease to exist as George Square.

However, only a few weeks later the Town's Planning Council did agree that, in effect, George Square would have to be given over to University development, even though they made certain conditions. This appears to have been a tribute not only to Appleton's advocacy but to the basic and undeniable University need. The main battle appeared to have been won and the University now turned to detailed planning, although progress was held up by one of Britain's perennial post-war economic crises. In 1954 the City of Edinburgh's Development Plan was the subject of a public inquiry at which objections were heard; but, significantly, none were raised to the allocation of George Square and its surrounding areas for "cultural, University and public buildings". Basil, now Sir Basil, Spence was appointed as special architectural adviser on the central development area. And in July 1955 the Town Council's Planning Committee gave final permission for the extension of the medical buildings in George Square—subject only to what appeared to be a minor item—"adjustment of the details of the facade of the building to their satisfaction on the lines indicated by Mr. Basil Spence".

Now, in the summer of 1955, it became evident that the University plans for George Square were more than a dream which would forever be kept from translation into reality by economic crises, argument with the City, or the various other impediments which had held up plans for almost a couple of decades. And now the opposition, persistent but so far subdued, began to increase its attacks into barrage proportions. Appleton, by virtue not only of his position, but of the way in which he had put the University's case in public, personally attracted much of the fire.

During this period the complexity of the battle-lines became clear, since opposition came not only from the amenity bodies and from individual citizens but from many inside the University itself. Heads of departments, junior staff, and former graduates were among those who wrote to Appleton, arguing that the destruction of George Square was too great a price to pay even for much-needed University expansion. His answers are revealing. It appears from their large number that he must have replied personally to most if not all of those who wrote; he replied, moreover, not with the stereotyped reply which many men might have considered adequate, but with carefully thoughtout letters dealing individually with the points raised.

To one graduate Appleton wrote a detailed three-page letter, arguing the case against her various proposals and ending with: "No, I fear that your letter does not make me alter my views one little bit. Sorry! But, again, let me say how nice it is to see someone caring so much for their Alma Mater." And to another he gave, in one central paragraph, the reasons which were to sustain him throughout the battle. "You are quite wrong when you say that the University is indifferent to other people's views which do not happen to coincide with their own," this went. "Moreover, when you say that the University's case is a weak one, I do not think you appreciate sufficiently the need to expand and improve, very substantially, the University's facilities for the century ahead of us, when student numbers will increase. I have here in mind, not only the effect of the high birth-rate after the war, but the general tendency to educate our young people better, for a world in which leisure will be increased."

He argued well. But he did not always succeed. And one of the most moving letters that he received came, in the summer of 1955, from his old mentor and colleague, C. T. R. Wilson, the man who more than half a century earlier had found, on the summit of Ben Nevis, the clues which were to lead to the cloud-chamber, now in his later eighties and living in retirement on the outskirts of Edinburgh. "Dear Appleton," he wrote. "I feel I must write to say how very sorry I am about this proposal to alter radically so irreplaceable a treasure as George Square. I find the arguments in favour of the plan quite unconvincing."

Many others felt the same, although during the latter half of 1955 it seemed unlikely that the plans could be further impeded. The University Grants Committee had allocated sufficient money. Final amendments were being made to the details of the medical buildings design. All seemed to be well.

Then, in January 1956, the situation altered. "On Monday last," Appleton wrote to Sir Basil Spence, "I got some grave news." This was that despite all the efforts that had been made to amend the plans, the Town Planning Committee had resolutely decided to reject them. And if it was impossible to start work even on the reconstruction which had generally been taken for granted, what would be the fate of the far more important plans for the rest of the Square?

To Appleton, the action struck at the very vitals of the University's future. As he had once put it in a letter to Sir Keith Murray, the University had "used the promise of the vista of new accommodation, according to our George Square Plan, as a kind of bait.... The essential point in all these matters is this: that, now that University salaries are practically uniform over the British Isles, we people in Scotland want to have attractive accommodation and other facilities to offer, when we are bidding in the general academic market." Now it appeared that all their plans might be thrown into the melting pot once again. Appleton's reaction was an almost perfect illustration of the decisive way in which he could, and did, act when necessary. More in sorrow than in anger, he drafted a letter to the Lord Provost, Sir John Banks, lamenting the fact that "here we are, held up over this question of architectural values, the Town Planning Committee *and* the Town Planning Officer pitting their opinion ... against that of *three* distinguished architects".

Then, to underline his position, he warned that unless something was done he would appeal to the Secretary of State for Scotland, standing firm entirely on the question of architectural integrity. The Lord Provost and the Town Clerk personally intervened. As Appleton wrote to Spence shortly afterwards: "You know the result. It is a lesson." The University had been given permission to proceed.

It is difficult not to feel that it was here, early in 1956, that the whole of the George Square scheme was finally pushed across the watershed by Appleton's action. The struggle was to go on, although from now onward it assumed more the character of a rear-guard, delaying action on the part of the opposition. The Secretary of State refused, in 1956, the plea for a public inquiry. But after the Town Council had, 3 years later, approved general plans for the buildings that were to replace the houses on two sides of the Square, opposition flared up again. The amenity societies appealed to the Secretary of State, Sir John Maclay, later Viscount Muirshiel; but following what Appleton himself described as "the welter of controversy", the Secretary of State supported the University. One individual's personal attempt to delay the University by legal intervention failed. The major demolitions in George Square then began, omens of the new University precinct into which the Square was to be transformed, and of the two tall tower blocks which were to obtrude on to the ancient, unique, skyline of the city.

Appleton lived long enough to see the start of the physical transformation, but not the end of the feelings aroused. When he opened the David Hume tower in 1963, one Scottish journal commented in terms which give some indication of the passions through which the Principal had had to pick a careful way. The opening, it was said, "reminds some of us very forcibly of the background manoeuvring, official obstinacy, nay downright stupidity, and frightful shiftiness that preceded the final agreement whereby the Corporation, with the connivance of the then Secretary of State, granted permission to the University to begin the despoliation of the City's largest, and in the truly Georgian sense, first example of urban planning".

Time, which heals most things, will presumably heal the wounds caused by the destruction of George Square. To those looking at the controversy from the outside three things seem perfectly clear. If the University was not to be surgically removed from the heart of the City at a cost, financial and psychological, which would have been immense, then the destruction of George Square was inevitable. Secondly, Appleton's handling of the unpleasant operation was carried out in such a way that the resulting scars on the relationship between the University and the rest of Edinburgh were fewer, and less serious, than might have been expected. One explanation for this was revealed in a letter which Appleton wrote to his old friend Professor Andrade in 1961. "I think I showed monumental patience – and courteous urbanity – in dealing with amenity societies who were anxious to deny us the right to build in George Square," he said. "We won; but have rather won our enemies over by refusing to claim a victory."

Finally, whatever the case for a George Square transformation of some kind, the resulting tower blocks have given the Edinburgh skyline a new feature that is freshly unique or damagingly incongruous according to taste.

CHAPTER 11

1949–1959: THE ELDER STATESMAN

THE Appleton who by the end of the 1950's had helped Edinburgh University over the hump towards the solution of its major problems of expansion was a man in many ways more sure of himself than the former secretary of the DSIR who had arrived in the city in 1949. He had been in command of a major organisation for 10 years and had already left his imprint on it. Had he died in 1959 there would still have been an Appleton era to be remembered at Edinburgh, different in quality from any that had gone before.

This quality was a direct reflection of Appleton himself and had something of his own contrasting qualities of kindliness and Victorian discipline. It was the kindliness that was remembered by scores of students, a kindliness obviously not tacked on to the man from outside, for the sake of appearances, but an essential part of the way he thought and moved and did his job.

One occasion at a reception for the freshmen in the Upper Library was typical. "I and a friend, gauche from the clutches of a girl's school in the depths of Fife, were cowering in a corner, wondering if we could ever find our feet in this vast University...", remembers one young woman. "We were both sunk in the depths of misery and were debating with ourselves whether we could ever communicate with this body of seemingly self-confident fellow students. At this point Sir Edward came up to us and began to chat in the most delightful way. He completely relaxed us till we found that we were once more our normal exuberant selves. From that time on, it was as though he had waved the proverbial magic wand, and my University career was a joy in every respect. I will never forget that the great man could take time to welcome two shy girls and put them at their ease. "

He was also a great finder of time — for addressing luncheon meetings, for the extensive committee work which was heaped upon him, or for writing to former University men. "I like to keep up a correspondence with Edinburgh graduates," he wrote. "So please never hesitate about writing. For some years now I have corresponded with the oldest graduates of all; but, alas, they pass on and there is an element of sadness about it all. Only a few years ago we lost our oldest graduate, who took his medical degree in 1880. Just think that one out. Some time afterwards I had a charming letter from his nurse who used to go over my letters with him . . . ."

He also found time to reply to unexpected correspondents such as the 12-year-old in the United States who wanted to become a scientist. To him, Appleton sent a two-page letter of advice, commenting: "Mathematics and English I would pick out, even at present, as essential subjects. I select English, as well, here, because the world manages its business by communications in words. Whatever you become when you are a man, scientist or non-scientist, you will have to express what you think to others by the spoken word or in writing. And you can improve your performance in both by constant practice — and by constant reading."

The habit of remembering in time the small things that most people remember too late, was not confined to his attitude to young people. If a member of the University staff was ill for more than a few days he or she would invariably receive a "get well" note from the Principal, often accompanied by the gift of a book which he thought the invalid might enjoy. When Lord Attlee dined at the University on one ceremonial occasion it was Appleton who remembered that the Labour leader did not smoke cigars, who ensured that there was placed beside the former Prime Minister, at just the right moment, a tin of what he had discovered was Attlee's favourite tobacco. And when Sir John Hunt, fresh from his conquest of Everest, came to speak at the University, Appleton noticed his chauffeur's interest in the mountaineer, and went out of his way to get Sir John's autograph for him.

His popularity with students was buttressed by his genuine feeling for sport, and on the coldest Saturday afternoon he could be seen at the Craiglockhart ground, a burly, wrapped-up, and keenly concerned spectator. He rarely missed the rugby internationals at Murrayfield where he became a familiar figure with the big cigar which he enjoyed so much poking out from between his felt hat and muffler. He also became a great watcher of sport on TV, looking forward to the major boxing matches and the football or cricket broadcasts. His interests stretched to athletics—for which he gave a handsome trophy to be competed for with Glasgow University—and he was not always recognised as he mixed with the crowds. On one dismal afternoon, when the mist was so thick that the timekeepers for the 200 yards could not see the starter's gun and had to go by sound alone, someone mentioned that this would alter the timing; and following Appleton's quick: "Yes, it'll be nought point six of a second faster", there came a voice from the back: "Who's the old bee with the high-powered mathematics?"

But it was cricket which continued to retain his strongest loyalty, and in August 1956 he wrote to *The Times* suggesting that cricket commentators should consider using "runs an over" rather than "runs an hour". The letter, published on 23 August, suggested that two runs per over might be taken as normal, and went on to assess some of the year's Test performances. Expressed in the suggested way, the rate of scoring would not only be independent of the widely different times taken by fast and slow bowlers but could "be calculated by the armchair cricketer, using the bowling analyses normally published". Cricket was sometimes introduced into the University Court, and on more than one occasion its meetings were interrupted by a messenger who entered with a sealed envelope for the Principal; inside was the latest Test score. Enthusiasm must finally have infected the others, since Appleton was later able to report, "A note of the Test score was circulated round the table at the last Court meeting."

It was natural that such a man should start the Cowan House race. Standing in George Square, the House was long used as a university hostel and there had been increasing protests from among the students at the time taken to reach the University from it. When an argument arose as to the exact time, Appleton suggested that the matter should be put to the test. And each year the 40 or 50 good walkers used to race from the building to the War Memorial at the top of the Old College quadrangle. Here the Principal awaited them—subsequently entertaining the winner and a guest to dinner.

Appleton's task at Edinburgh was eased by his natural interests; but it was further helped by certain lines of policy which he laid down for himself. Perhaps the most valuable of these—born, no doubt, of what he had seen from Whitehall during the war—was not to be drawn into the personal arguments and vendettas which from time to time scrape across the scientific world much as they scrape across others. His method was exemplified when he received a long letter of complaint from an old colleague. Appleton's support was required, but it seemed that a personal row would almost inevitably follow. He remembered how Whistler had sent a similar letter on a comparable occasion and he remembered how the recipient had replied with a simple card: "Not for me, Jimmie." Appleton did likewise. Thus he avoided major arguments. The nearest that he came to personal involvement was when friends or colleagues visited Edinburgh and failed to call upon him. As one colleague put it, "While he was in many ways a man of steel, he could be curiously affected by the minor pin-pricks of life." A failure to call on the Principal was one of them. This weakness sprang, no doubt, from his belief that the office of Principal should always be treated with due respect and dignity, a necessary counter-balance to the freedom that the times demanded. Thus when one visiting professor looked with some surprise at the official car and the Vice-Chancellor's pennon flying from the bonnet, Appleton nodded: "It looks prestigious, doesn't it. It's meant to."

This attitude illustrated the other side of the Appleton which Edinburgh had got to know; the formality, the "correctness" in an almost German sense of the word, that would have looked pompous in any man standing on his dignity for dignity's sake. His striped trousers, his Eden hat, his stiff collar and his sober tie—"I like," he once said, "to be well-dressed in the style before last"—became a sign of his presence in Edinburgh as they had in Whitehall. Appleton appeared thus, in what was sometimes referred to as his uniform, at conferences, at international meetings, at scientific gatherings where informality, if not unconformity, was often the order of the day, and he was rigorous in upholding what he considered to be the necessary proprieties. In Brussels one summer he looked in shocked wonder across the cafeteria while lunching with a number of colleagues. "Do you see that?" he asked in astonishment. His friends looked to where an equally eminent but more informal elder statesman of the ionosphere had taken off his jacket and put it across the back of his chair while he continued his meal in braces. Appleton got up, walked across, spoke a few words, and returned to his table. The miscreant obediently put on his jacket.

This attitude, which at times verged on primness, was reflected in his conversation both private and public. He "liked a joke" but tended to keep them within the bounds of pre-war rather than post-war taste. He had no sympathy at all for the over-risqué story, and his general attitude is well illustrated by the draft of his talk for the BBC on "Science and Industry". In this he had written "... the man in the street (I do not include the woman in the street for fear of being misunderstood)". Then, on second thoughts, he had deleted the parenthesis.

At times his personal views were in conflict with his ideas of University liberty, as when Professor Carstairs gave the Reith lectures in 1963. Appleton found some of these difficult to stomach and would turn in indignation to his friends commenting: "But the man's actually advocating free love!" However, when a correspondent wrote to him complaining that one of his professors had been allowed to speak as he did, Appleton replied by saying that he agreed with the writer. But he felt forced to add: "But you will surely understand that a University is a place where both thought and speech are free. It is under such conditions that Professor Carstairs has felt able to say what he thinks...."

By the end of Appleton's first decade at Edinburgh it was natural that anyone whose interests were linked to the University or its reputation or its prospects should find themselves in correspondence with him. He had become identified with the University in such a complete sense that it was easy to overlook his continuing scientific work, his influence in the international field, or his position as what is frequently called "a statesman of science".

In all these fields his work from 1949 was largely a continuation of what had gone before. The same is true of his connections with defence where in 1949 there appeared a curious and unexpected echo from the past. The two gentlemen whose "television-to-beat-the-bombers" scheme had been investigated in such detail by Appleton and Smith-Rose in the winter of the blitz had now lodged a claim against the War Office for the impounding of another prototype earlier in 1940, and Appleton was called in to give expert advice.

His work with or for the Services was naturally enough of a more limited kind than it had been a decade earlier. However, the growth of the cold war and the ever more complicated schemes of electronic measure, counter-measure, and counter-counter-measure made his advice of use in a number of ways. In 1951 he was brought on to Lord Hankey's revived Technical Personnel Committee. He was a member of various advisory defence bodies which sat from time to time, and he performed various other services for the authorities for which both his technical experience and his political leanings especially fitted him.

As the war-time head of the DSIR he was frequently asked for comments on the nuclear developments of the 1950's. His position is bluntly put by a prepared statement which he issued for the *Daily Mail* and the United States Information Services in April 1954. "Sir Edward Appleton said that in wartime discussions about the Atomic Bomb even before it became a reality, he and his scientist colleagues had expressed the hope that in the end it might stop war for ever," this went. "This was still his hope and for that reason he greatly welcomed the Hydrogen Bomb as being something likely to make an aggressor pause. His confidence in American intentions was such that the more and bigger Atomic Bombs they had the safer every peace loving citizen ought to feel. He hoped that the present concern would revive interest in the possibility of the international control of Atomic Energy but such control was no use unless the controlling body had free access for inspection everywhere — throughout Russia for example as well as throughout America."

Whatever his involvement on the fringe of nuclear politics, his continuing interests lay in the upper atmosphere, in ensuring that even if his idea of a postgraduate school in Edinburgh must remain forever unfulfilled, he would still press on with his own investigation of the ionosphere. In this he had the full co-operation of the University. When the Curators of Patronage had appointed him they had stressed that a continuation of his scientific work would be welcome; a room had subsequently been made available above the Vice-Chancellor's own office; and here there had been installed his own computational assistant — Mrs. Turnbull.

By June 1950 he was able to report progress. His continuing idea had been to gain more detailed knowledge of the ionosphere's morphology, of the form, shape, thickness, and structure of the ionised belts which encircle the earth like the skin round an onion. He had concentrated on F_2 anomalies and had been able to throw light on its sunspot cycle variation, on the position of the ionospheric equator in the F_2-Layer, and on the world morphology of the layer's equivalent heights. He had been able to show that the currently held view that the intensity of solar photons produced the layer was almost certainly wrong, and he had continued the work started earlier with Piggott on the subject of ionospheric storms. "I have," he wrote, "been fortunate in the response to my appeals to ionospheric stations all over the world to send me their routine results, and these have been my basic material."

This raw material came to him from Slough, from Washington, from Germany, Tokyo, and Australia. It came, in fact, from virtually all the ionospheric sounding stations which had by this time been set up across the world. The thick envelopes containing their masses of tabulated figures did not come only because Appleton was still an important figure in URSI — the President until 1952 as well as the holder of many other posts. He was also, until forced off by pressure of work, a member of the Radio Research Board; he was also, of course, the greatest British expert on the ionosphere, so that the data came to Edinburgh, addressed to Appleton, almost as though to an international institution. He used this material, which continued to flow into his rooms for the rest of his life, to make a number of significant discoveries.

These were not comparable with his pin-pointing of the ionosphere's height and his discovery of the Appleton Layer a quarter of a century earlier or with his development of the magneto-ionic theory. But they were nevertheless of much scientific interest, and they would have been noteworthy had they been made by a man with no other responsibilities, let alone a man bearing a heavy University burden. But as Appleton explained in a letter to a colleague, "I am sure that if you really have a deep love for science, you can keep pegging away at research in spite of other duties."

This "pegging-away", as with most other things that Appleton did, was exceedingly well organised. It was carried out in two different ways. One was by means of a simple collaboration with former colleagues such as Piggott and Beynon, with whom he would discuss various theories by letter, and with whom he would subsequently work out the necessary details – often in long bouts of concentrated discussion. Secondly, he utilised the services of one or more ionospheric workers on a continuing basis in his own University office, frequently paid for by Royal Society or Radio Research Board grants. Thus for a considerable while Mrs. Turnbull carried out the bulk of the mathematical work involved.

Another worker was A. J. Lyons, later Professor of Physics in Ibadan and at the University of Hong Kong, a man whose involvement with Appleton was typical. In 1952 Appleton had given a series of lectures on the ionosphere to a group of students working at Edinburgh for a postgraduate diploma in electronics, speaking to them for the first hour every morning for a week and showing a great delight, as one of his colleagues put it, "in getting back to the blackboard". Lyon, who was one of these students, was so swept up that he applied to help Appleton as a research assistant, was taken on and then worked with him for 3 years. "He was always very kind to me, and I found my association with him helpful in many ways," he says. "He introduced me to the literature of the subject and to many of the outstanding scientists working in ionospheric physics. I found him a very stimulating person to work with and met him frequently, sometimes daily at coffee in the morning, for discussions of what I was doing. He greatly enjoyed laying aside the administrative affairs which were his main concern, to spend a quarter of an hour or so talking about the ionosphere, and I know that he often spent the evenings working or thinking about ionospheric problems. I believe he found this a pleasant relaxation from his other duties."

PLATE 21A.   (*above*) With H.R.H. Prince Philip, Chancellor of the University of Edinburgh (by courtesy of *The Scotsman*).

PLATE 21B.   (*below*) At the opening of the Cameron House Youth Centre, Edinburgh University Settlement, 1961 (by courtesy of *The Scotsman*).

PLATE 22A. (*above*) A typical after-dinner speech (*by courtesy of* Photo Illustrations (Scotland)).

PLATE 22B. (*below*) With Professor Van der Pol, Chairman of the URSI Commission on Radio Waves and Circuits, 1948–1952, right, and Professor W. N. Christiansen at the 10th URSI General Assembly, Sydney, 1952.

PLATE 23A. (*top right*) After the special graduation ceremony to confer an Hon.LLD. on Sir Vivien Fuchs; left to right, The University Bedellus, Captain E. G. Elder, Sir Vivien Fuchs, Sir Edward Appleton, The Rt. Hon. Sir Ian Johnson-Gilbert, Lord Provost of Edinburgh, Dr. James Robertson Justice, Rector of the University (*by courtesy of* E. R. Yerbury & Son).

PLATE 23B.   (*below*) Sir Edward Appleton and C. T. R. Wilson at Wilson's 90th Birthday Luncheon, 1959 (*by courtesy of* George Outram & Co.).

PLATE 24A. (*above*) Sir Edward Appleton and Mrs. Helen Allison, later Lady Appleton, opening the Wind Tunnel, Natural Philosophy Department, University of Edinburgh, 1965 (*by courtesy of* Beaverbrook Newspapers).

PLATE 24B. (*left*) Abden House, Edinburgh, official residence of the Principal of Edinburgh University.

This "pleasant relaxation" was to produce some thirty papers and notes, a number of the earliest dealing with the effect of magnetic storms on the ionosphere. At Edinburgh Appleton was receiving information from a far greater proportion of the world than had previously been the case; and now, as he put it, it became "possible to consider storm morphology for the world as a whole and reconcile the results, which have previously been unco-ordinated, from stations at different magnetic latitudes". The results were revealing, for they showed what had not previously been shown—that the general effect of such storms was to exaggerate the distortions in the F_2-Layer which were a permanent effect of the earth's permanent magnetic field. Some of these results he described first in letters to friends. Thus in the summer of 1954 he wrote to Van der Pol about "a most remarkable effect I have discovered on the magnetic equator. I found, in the war, that F_2 ionisation was subject to geomagnetic control, and, in 1946, published a curve showing how N_{max} is distributed over the world at noon." This curve showed a trough. "I now find that [this] trough at the magnetic equator alters very materially during the day; and, at midnight, it is a crest." The width of this anomalous belt, which followed the magnetic equator round the earth, was between 2000 and 3000 miles across, Appleton went on, and was not only of theoretical but also of great practical interest.

He was always anxious to stress the University's part in these discoveries, made under the direction and guidance which he gave during time slotted in between his other work. Thus it was typical that when he broadcast on "The future in international science" in December 1955, he should use as an illustration of his theme the recent "scientific discovery made in Edinburgh University". With the help of two colleagues, he went on, he had "found evidence of a large-scale electrical current system circulating in the upper atmosphere, sixty miles above ground level. This electric current flows in a large circle, flowing from west to east over the Equator and from east to west over Great Britain." According to Appleton's thinking, this current, whose existence Balfour Stewart had postulated more than half a century earlier, would be produced naturally enough by the horizontal tidal motion of the ionosphere—which he had detected earlier—acting as a moving electrical conductor in the presence of the earth's permanent magnetic field. "Now it is a familiar truth of the elementary theory of electromagnetism," he said later, "that an electrical current element, moving in a magnetic field, experiences a mechanical force—at right angles to both the current element and the magnetic field directions." And with the ionospheric current passing from east to west across Britain most strongly at about 11 each morning, and with the magnetic field direction to the north, then the current—and the ionosphere which carried it—would be forced downwards. This, following examination of data collected by Slough, was exactly what was found: during the hour between 11 and noon the height of the E-Layer was regularly drawn significantly downwards.

Much of such work was by now being described in what was soon known throughout the world as "Appleton's Journal". In 1949 he had written to David Brunt, Secretary of the Royal Society, to Beynon, Smith-Rose of Slough, Harang in Norway, and a number of other colleagues. "I wish to consult you privately about a proposal which I have been turning over in my mind for some time," he said. "It is that there should be formed in Britain an international journal with some such title as the 'Journal of Terrestrial Physics'. We badly need a journal which will ensure prompt publication of the great body of work now being done in our own and allied fields." Butterworth–Springer would be willing to publish the journal if there were assurances of support from the scientific world, and Appleton went on to ask for suggestions of title, frequency of publication and so on. *JATP—The Journal of Atmospheric and Terrestrial Physics*— was started the following year.

Appleton took particular pride in his own frequent contributions to the journal, and when he was finishing one of them little could push the details entirely from his mind. There was, for instance, the occasion in 1956 when HM the Queen and HRH Prince Philip (who had been installed as Chancellor of the University three years previously), attended a performance of *The Magic Flute* given by the Hamburg State Opera at the King's Theatre, during the Edinburgh Festival. Sir Edward was amongst the Lord Provost's party. While everyone was absorbed in the music he slipped a pencil from his pocket and began to write a short paragraph and a complicated equation on the programme. The following morning he pinged the bell in his office. "When I went," says Mrs. Allison, "he said: 'Well, that's the end of the paper!' Then he handed me the theatre programme of the previous evening with the end of the technical argument written out on the back of it."

The almost Olympian viewpoint from which he could regard the whole range of ionospheric problems is well brought out by a typical letter to Piggott. "This letter is to tie up the strings of our talk," he began.

"(1) I am sufficiently in research funds to be able to spend £50 on the $D(fF2)/Q(fF2)$ work we discussed. Indeed there would be no difficulty in spending a bit more! So please go ahead, if you can arrange things with Mrs. Moorhouse.

"We agree that it would be best to start with equatorial stations (four years' averages for Equinox, Northern Solstice and Southern Solstice) and work north.

"I am sending you a note herewith, by Fung Chien, about storms at Taipei. The heart of the matter is shown on Figure (8) and Figure (9). This suggests to me that, as we go south from temperate latitudes, our 1000 h. minimum begins to occur earlier in local time. But there must be an enormous, and rapid change, between Taipei and the magnetic equator!

"(2) Bell [who worked for Appleton for a considerable while] has given me the actual figures of Δt for the graphs you saw. I was glad to see that you were impressed with our method of showing the effect of the 'equation of time'.

"But something has clearly gone wrong at Inverness during April and July 1958. I think you took away a note of this.

"(3) As you know I have been bothered for a long time about our general statement, in our big storm paper, that 'ionospheric storms are essentially uni-polar'. I have been doubtful about this from the start, but you seemed certain that it was right.

"Ought we not to correct it in some way?

"(4) If you have any further suggestions for material I could include in the British Association lecture 'Science and Communication' I should be grateful to learn of them. I am well aware of past history, but it will be nice to bring in more modern points like information theory etc. However, there will only be time for brief, but telling, references. I am looking for a good striking example of a message which is very distorted in transmission, but which is still intelligible! Probably Farvis can help here."

This continuing interest with the characteristics of the invisible layers that encircled the earth all ran back to the somewhat mysterious genius Oliver Heaviside, and it was therefore with unusual delight that Appleton read one morning a letter placed on his desk by Mrs. Allison. The first sentence was startling enough—"I have a sackful of Oliver Heaviside's papers in my garage." The rest was worthy of the beginning. The writer, a science master in the West Country, explained how when visiting friends at Paignton, he had been told that a scientist called Heaviside once lived in the house, and that many scientific papers still lay under the floor boards in the attic. "The following morning," the letter went on, "I pulled up one floor board and the truth of the statement was confirmed. The papers were almost exclusively in Heaviside's handwriting. They were written on the back of bills, mainly from Music publishers and Musical Instrument makers. There are galley proofs of his books and articles, some uncorrected except for occasional errors in punctuation; some have his work written all over the back. There are a few, very few, personal notes, but they include some postcards from Sir Oliver Lodge and a communication from Lord Kelvin. The condition of the papers is somewhat grim, but in the main they are fairly dry, though terribly dusty, and about 90% are easily legible." The schoolmaster had heard of Appleton's broadcast during the Heaviside Centenary Celebrations a few years earlier and had written to him at once. Appleton, "both excited and delighted", immediately ensured that the papers were properly studied and preserved.

The determination with which he pressed on with his beloved ionospheric work was equalled by his determination to remain close to URSI's international machinery. As President until 1952, and as head of one or more of its committees for much longer, he was deeply involved in a heavy correspondence stretching across the world; in advising, suggesting, mentioning the names of men for possible work, commenting on how this problem might be handled or that particular aspect of scientific inquiry conducted. He was also drawn into a number of journeys abroad—notably to URSI's general assemblies at Zurich in 1950, Sydney in 1952, The

Hague in 1954, and Boulder, Colorado, in 1957. In such cases universities or scientific bodies in the country visited usually asked Appleton to speak, thus adding to his task of preparing a presidential address, bearing the burden of the social round, and playing his inevitable part in background lobbying. These calls on him as a visiting lecturer were only equalled by his lack of available time, as the Canadians found when they invited him in 1954. He had to refuse, postponed the invitation until 1955, postponed it again until 1956, had to admit that he was "a slippery fish to land", postponed it once again until 1957, and finally found time to visit Canada only in 1958 when he attended the Commonwealth Universities Congress.

URSI's Australian meeting of 1952, which he attended with his wife and younger daughter, provided a good illustration of the demands made on him. On this occasion he addressed the 29th meeting of the Australian Association for the Advancement of Science, attended the Sydney Centenary Celebrations as the Edinburgh University delegate, gave the War Memorial Lecture to the Sydney University Engineering Club, and also chaired the Third Meeting of the Mixed Commission on the Ionosphere which was held during the same summer period in Canberra. And it was only natural that on the journey out Appleton should be nobbled by the Captain of the *Strathmore* to speak to the passengers on "The challenge of scientific progress". In addition, he broke his return voyage at Adelaide—having to land via ship's ladder and pilot launch after the ship had been delayed by bad weather—to give a public lecture on the role of science in defence and industry.

On their return home in the *Orcades*, Appleton and his wife indulged in mild sightseeing when the ship put into port, visited the Governor of Gibraltar whom they had known in Edinburgh, handled the famous Keys, and got special permission to visit the labyrinthine galleries cut into the Rock. On this return journey they were not accompanied by their daughter. For on the journey out Rosalind had fallen in love with the purser of the *Strathmore*, a young officer who had studied at Magdalen. She insisted on returning on the same ship and married her purser by special licence in Edinburgh soon after the ship docked: so that, as Appleton wrote to his family in Bradford, "now we've two daughters connected with the sea — one Royal Navy and the other Merchant Navy".

The Australian meeting had witnessed the setting-up of one fresh international committee of which Appleton was to become President and whose activities were to involve him in a vast amount of additional work. This was the URSI—IGY Committee, the organisation which would be responsible for all aspects of radio investigation throughout the International Geophysical Year, due to start in 1957.

The idea for such a special observational year had first been proposed early in 1950 by Dr. L. V. Berkner at an informal meeting of a small group of scientists in the United States. Initially, the plan was for a "Third Polar Year", to be 25 rather than 50 years after the Second Polar Year of 1932–3 and it was a proposal for this which was put to the second meeting of the Mixed Commission on the Ionosphere which met under Appleton's chairmanship in Brussels on 4 September 1950. Appleton supported the idea for a number of reasons, one being that 1957–8 would be a year of maximum sunspot activity and thus particularly important for ionospheric observations. The meeting approved a memorandum calling for the Third International Polar Year, and this was sent on its way to the four unions represented on the Mixed Commission and to the International Council of Scientific Unions.

From 1950 the idea blossomed out. It was agreed that the work should be extended to cover not merely the polar areas but the whole world, and Appleton was made chairman of the body responsible for the radio observations. In 1954, after each of the countries involved had set up its own committee to correlate national work in different fields, Appleton was offered the chairmanship of the British National Committee in place of the then chairman who wished to retire due to frequent absences abroad. "There is nothing I would like more...", Appleton replied from Edinburgh, "but I just ought not to take it on for lack of time. I am penned down here with many other duties and I would not be able to do full justice to the work involved. It is just a cast of logistics—unfortunately."

Nevertheless, he was to be fully enough involved, not only with the organisation of the radio work, but with publicising and explaining it to the people of Britain through articles and broadcasts. At an early stage he had suggested—unsuccessfully—that when speaking or writing of the International Geophysical Year, everyone involved should "use the

French form of initials and pronounce it 'EEGA' which is near enough to the English word 'eager' to have a certain appropriate significance". This illustrated his whole approach to the operation which was finally carried out in 1957–8 with the co-operation of nearly forty countries. "Although perhaps we did not think of it at the time," he wrote in referring to the Brussels meeting at which the idea had formally been put forward for the first time, "we now realise that much more than the progress of science is involved. For one thing, secrecy between nations will here be out of place, and it should be easy to agree on the pooling and exchange of scientific information." And in broadcasting about the Year he stressed his constant delight "to see these representatives of many nations – nations from Europe, Africa, Asia, Australia and America, all of them, pooling their ideas and resources without suspicion or jealousy".

This purely international character of the IGY intrigued Appleton almost as much as the valuable scientific results which were achieved. So much so that late in 1958 he succeeded in having ICSU, the International Union responsible for the IGY, nominated for the Nobel Peace Prize. This echoed back to an earlier proposal when he had felt that the Edinburgh Festival Society should be nominated for the prize, on the ground that it was "a most potent force for international peace and understanding, in that it appeals to the similarities, and not the differences between nations". Appleton had tried to obtain government support for the submission but had been warned that as the Festival helped the balance of payments "governmental sponsorship of a submission might lead to some embarrassment and perhaps some rather uncharitable comment".

The idea that ICSU might be a contestant for the Peace Prize was on a totally different level of credibility, and comparable precedents already existed in awards to the International Committee of the Red Cross, to the Society of Friends, and the United Nations High Commission for Refugees. It was an idea entirely Appleton's, and during the latter half of 1958 he drew up, with the Astronomer-Royal, Sir Harold Spencer-Jones, a detailed memorandum which early in 1959 was submitted to the Nobel Committee of the Norwegian Parliament by Lord Boyd-Orr, the winner of the Nobel Peace Prize in 1949. The nomination outlined the genesis of ICSU and the growth of its membership to a total of sixty-six countries. It explained how more than 2000 stations, spread across the world, had taken part in the IGY and how the massive accumulation of data gathered by them was to be made freely available at three World Data Centres, in the United States, in Russia, and in Europe. And towards the end of the 24-page document there came the key paragraph which was not only the basis of the nomination but one explanation of Appleton's continuing interest in the operation. "The many nations of diverse race, colour, religion and political organization that have joined harmoniously and freely together in the scientific study of the earth and the sun during the eighteen months of the IGY have given proof that, however many and serious are the political problems that trouble the human race, it is possible for the nations to work together in a great enterprise planned for the common good. Thus, by example, it has proved to be of encouragement to peaceful co-operation in other fields of activity."

Appleton's position in this international field was equalled by the position he held by this time in the British scientific establishment. In the lobbying and discussions that preceded the election of new Fellows to the Royal Society he was one of those whose opinion was most frequently canvassed. "I am keen on seeing good people from industry getting in," he once wrote of such elections. "I have always resented the charge that 'it is only applied work'; for the real test is: 'Is it original?' Rutherford, I'm glad to say, took much the same view."

He was closely associated with the Society's work in other ways, notably in those areas where it was knotted to the Government in general and to the University Grants Committee in particular in the financing of science. With his own lengthening record of administration and experience in public life he must have seemed a likely choice for the presidency; but his heavy burden nearly 400 miles north of London was a handicap, and although at one period he stated he would be willing to return to London were he elected, his voice was either not raised strongly enough or went unheeded.

Nevertheless, throughout the 1950's more than one of the expected honours came his way including, in 1953, the presidency of the British Association. He had been closely connected with the Association when its meeting had been held under H.R.H. Prince Philip in Edinburgh in 1951 and had in fact played a significant part in the successful televising of the key events. Some sessions were to be held in the McEwan Hall, others in the Usher Hall; a land-line had to be laid between the two halls, and it was taken for granted that the GPO would give the necessary permission for this. Only a short while before the meeting was to start it was learned that the Post Office was putting down its foot: no land-line. This refusal might have been effective against anyone who lacked a detailed knowledge of what was technologically possible and legally unpreventable. "Fine," said Appleton, "but if permission is not granted for a land-line I shall personally apply for an Inventor's licence. This cannot be refused, and when I have got it I will see that a line is laid." He got the permission.

The 1953 meeting was to be held in Liverpool and this in itself presented him with a particularly daunting challenge. It had for long been the custom for the presidential address to link recent scientific advances with a philosophic or ethical theme, and those who had presided over previous meetings in the city included Huxley, Lister, and Rutherford, a formidable trio to find oneself matched against. Appleton took even more care than usual in worrying out what he should talk about and in preparing his address. Someone had suggested "The science of humanism" which he agreed "certainly looks good but... does not sufficiently convey the idea of Science as a pleasurable occupation". He had already begun to react against what he regarded as the contemporary Gadarene rush for material prosperity and, as he wrote to one friend, he wished "to raise science above the 'comfort-grinding machine' level where so many people seem to place it". When he began to think along these lines he realised that the work required would help him to sort out his own ideas about the real benefits of science. "My topic," he wrote to a friend in the BBC—which was to broadcast the address "live"—"will almost certainly deal with science as a culture and as an adventure leading to the enlargement of our knowledge of ourselves and of the universe in which we live. It will be a case of science for science's sake—and *not* science as harnessed for man's material benefit." And in his words to another old friend there is the suggestion that he had qualifications about current demands for a greater production of science graduates. "It seems," he wrote, "that, during recent years, there has been far too much emphasis on the social implications of science and not enough attention to Science itself. I want to bring out Science as a discipline which enlarges our horizons...."

This he no doubt did, in "Science for its own sake", one of the most successful of all British Association addresses and one in which he illustrated his theme by describing the immensely intriguing but materially irrelevant progress of radio astronomy which could "enlarge men's horizons and invest the world with deeper significance". At the same time Appleton stressed both the non-utilitarian essentials of science for its own sake—the "passionate desire to explore and understand" as he described it—and its unexpected philosophical rewards.

"Perhaps the most striking fact about modern science, in its explorations ranging from the heart of the atom to the frontiers of the universe," he said, "is that, like poetry, like philosophy, it reveals depths and mysteries beyond—and, this is important, quite different from—the ordinary matter-of-fact world we are used to. Science has given back to the universe, one might say, that quality of inexhaustible richness and unexpectedness and wonder which at one time it seemed to have taken away from it."

If Appleton had been expecting to touch a chord in a non-materialistic public, he seems to have succeeded. The BBC's listener research investigations showed that "Science for its own sake" had a higher "appreciation index" than the average for home talks, and a higher figure than any of the immediately earlier British Association addresses—not excluding A. V. Hill's "The ethical dilemma of science", the Duke of Edinburgh's address in 1951, or Sir Henry Tizard's "The passing world".

A set-piece address of the British Association variety was the ideal vehicle for a man such as Appleton who wished to make science and its aims understood by as many as possible, a man perhaps a little doubtful of the trends which science was taking and of the ever-increasing pressures being put upon it by Government in the name of social implications. But his views were also put over in a number of other speeches and lectures and broadcasts—particularly broadcasts, which he had been making since 1925 when he had given a Radio Society talk on "Fading". They included many talks to schools, a number of items in *Science Survey*, personal reminiscences of Rutherford, and more than one talk explaining the aims and methods of the International Geophysical Year. He was also one of three speakers—the others being Ed Murrow and Sir Eric Ashby—who launched the British Association Granada Lectures in 1959.

In 1956 he was invited to give the BBC Reith Lectures, and to deal with science and technology in Britain's national life, "taking acount of the pressing need for scientists and technologists and the various educational problems which are currently under discussion". Appleton accepted within a few days—"doubtless rashly", as he wrote to a friend at the National Physical Laboratory. "I could hardly refuse. But it means that I just have to cut out all extra-mural activities, or the lectures won't get done; for the preparations will involve a vast amount of reading and study. Indeed, I am beginning to wonder how I shall manage even then, so preoccupying are my University duties." And to Piggott he wrote rather despairingly: "I am afraid that the Reith Lectures are rather interfering with the ionosphere."

During the months that followed he wrote to scores of friends and former colleagues, gathering facts, asking for advice, putting up intellectual Aunt Sallies as their targets, probing the scientific and technological climate of the mid-1950's for the purpose he had in mind. Luckily, all the thick files which grew as he prepared the material for the lectures have been kept intact; from them one gains not only a clear idea of the morphology of such a series of lectures but also a sharp picture of Appleton in his early sixties.

"As tentative suggestions as regard the subject matter, it seems to me that I might draw much on my own personal experiences as a scientist, especially as regards illustrations," he replied to the Director-General of the BBC after a few weeks' thought. "In other words, I think it desirable for me to speak as much as possible from the inside—to appear to be 'in the business' (as they say on the stage). Next I would suggest that the task should have some missionary colouring—that I should get over, not only the national need for more scientists and technologists, but also should convey (say, to senior 'teenagers' and *all* parents) something of the satisfaction of a scientific career. Particularly would I like to engage 'the interest and enthusiasms of young people'."

There was a good deal of brooding about what the lectures were to be called. "The spirit and power of science", "Science as a vocation", "The aims and achievements of science" were all tentatively considered by Appleton, who responded to the BBC's suggestion of "The lead in science" with the comment that it seemed to him "Olympic Games-ish". Eventually, it was decided that the general title would be "Science and the Nation".

Early in 1956 Appleton began writing to the directors of the various research stations for which he had been responsible at the DSIR. He asked for their views; perhaps more important, he replied at length to their suggestions, and from the replies one can get a firm idea of the philosophical point at which Appleton had by this time arrived. There were many problems with which he was to deal in the Reith Lectures, particularly that of communication between scientist and non-scientist. But the real problems, which he tended to skirt with some circumspection, were more basic. One dealt with the moral responsibility of the scientist on this; his position was stated in a letter to the director of one research station: "You have clearly put your finger on a fundamental issue, and one which I can't say I've yet resolved entirely myself," he wrote. "As scientists we claim that we are sufficiently intelligent to be conscious of the consequences of our work. By contrast we could say that the same would not apply to a man who puts rivets in a submarine which, in the event, is to be used to sink neutral passenger ships. If the user declares his intent in advance we, perhaps, know where we are.

"But, without such a declaration of evil intent, one can often see a certain neutrality in our work.... We could imagine a thermo-nuclear bomb being used to blast an ice-floe so as to make an entry for the Theron, the research vessel engaged on law-abiding duties. By contrast, a powerful radio sending station could be used for the transmission of lies and for the excitement of hatred and distrust. Where are we in the matter? And at what stage, and in what way, should the scientist refuse to co-operate?

"It does seem to me that, without a declared user intent, there is a neutrality about scientific work. I have not been able to think of any scientific development that had exclusively evil uses. Yet I don't feel entirely satisfied about my thinking. Can you help?"

Appleton's dilemma was strikingly revealed by his own draft of a broadcast recorded for the BBC's European Service in the summer of 1959. He started by reiterating that "science is too serious a matter to be left entirely to the scientists". He thought that the scientists should state "and state loudly and clearly", his own views concerning the use of scientific knowledge. Nevertheless, he did not think that the scientist should suppress publication of his findings on the ground that others might use them evilly. "However," he concluded, "there are situations, especially in applied science, where the *use* of an end product has openly been declared, for example in the design of lethal weapons of war. In such cases I think we must recognise the right of a scientist to be a conscientious objector and to with-hold his co-operation." To that conclusion he added two "alternative endings". In one his last sentence concluded with "...with-hold his co-operation even if we do not ourselves agree with him". And in the second alternative he concluded by adding the sentence: "But, of course, the situation in this connection would differ, for most scientists, according to whether their own country was being threatened with aggression or not."

Early in 1956 he opened a large, black Reith Lectures notebook and throughout the spring and summer filled it with jottings such as: "Science may save us exposure to great risks, but not from the consequences of our folly" — "There is a certain technique in salesmanship necessary in selling science" — and "When people talk to me about scientific management I do not know what they mean." He was deeply involved in the industrial applications of science and believed, like Tizard, one of his predecessors at the DSIR, that great benefits would follow the better application of existing knowledge. The scientists themselves were largely to blame, and to one research director he wrote of how he believed "that many more scientists and technologists would arrive in the Board Room if they only were articulate in the right way — in both the written and spoken word". He repeated his belief that some scientists appeared to have as their motto: "Here's the truth: let's hide it," and to another correspondent he wrote despairingly: "I thought of saying that the scientist has got to forget his own 'short-hand' and speak to others in the ordinary 'longhand' of human intercourse. But so many scientists are unable to do this." There were, moreover, no short cuts. "I doubt myself whether special courses in English will help," he wrote. "To my mind a vocabulary comes from one's general reading, and to be able to use it with ease is a matter of practice."

Eventually, all was ready and the six lectures (on "Our national need of science"; "Science in war"; "Science for its own sake"; "Government science"; "Industrial science"; and "Science and education") were delivered throughout November and December. Appleton had insisted that the normal practice of the Reith Lecturer giving at least the last of the lectures in London should be broken in his case. He had none of the non-scientist's fear that because he was outside London his voice would be transmitted any less adequately.

The lectures were a considerable success. They were homely and down-to-earth, qualities that Reith Lecturers sometimes lacked, and to any who might have felt that their intellectual level was lower than normal Appleton would no doubt have replied as he commented to Lord Reith — "I counted the average parent or schoolmaster as my typical listener."

It was natural that he should reply personally to the scores of letters he received—to those which condemned the lectures as well as to those who praised them, to the correspondents who wanted Appleton to support an anti-war crusade, to those eaten up by their private crankeries, and to those who simply asked for advice. And to the listener who had apparently expected a Third Programme series, he concluded a long explanatory letter by saying: "Still, I admire the way you have thought about these problems and although I think your theory is wrong I count it to be a very ingenious and intelligent one." He replied with great interest to the man who revealed that the lectures had triggered off an idea for an interesting defence device; and to four pages of abuse which complained of "Our lovely old houses turned into hideous laboratories for *you* to carry out your beastly experiments in!!" he replied: "Dear Mrs. S—, Your letter is, you know, really a very rude one. Moreover, you say things which are not true. You speak of my beastly experiments. So I ask you if you would be good enough to read what I enclose. If, as I gather, you are so angry as not to be willing to read and listen, perhaps you would just *glance* at the marked paragraph on page 111. Yours very sincerely." When it came to human nature, Appleton remained an optimist.

The Elder Statesman

By the end of the 1950's it was clear that he would remain at Edinburgh for the rest of his working life. He had, in fact, become almost a part of the City. "You will know the position of a Principal in a Scottish University town," he wrote to his old friend, Professor Andrade. "If he is prepared to throw himself into local affairs—turning up at functions, making speeches and so on—he can be the second citizen to the Lord Provost himself. You will also know how much care I take over my speeches."

It was in almost every way an enviable position. Like most men, Appleton had not achieved everything he wished to achieve. But like Geoffrey Young, the mountaineer whose leg was shattered at the crest of his climbing career, he did "not grudge the little left undone".

There was, moreover, much still to accomplish. When it came to the ionosphere one could still, in spite of all the progress since 1924, echo Rutherford in a different field—"a grand subject because there is so much in it we don't know".

CHAPTER 12

1960–1965: THE FINAL YEARS

APPLETON's position a decade after his appointment as Principal in Edinburgh is illustrated by a letter he wrote to a friend in the Royal Society in March 1959. "I am still struggling, well behind in time, with my share of the introduction to the publication of Rutherford's papers," he said, referring to a paper on Rutherford's early years, "and I am then to run into the usual spate of speeches and lectures of the summer, with Edinburgh a milieu of the BMA and the Canadian MA Congress in July/August. I just dare not add to my agenda."

Somehow he succeeded in riding the waves. However numerous the tasks, however worrying the problems tossed up by the University, family life, or some quirk of research, he managed to retain his equanimity. An orderly mind helped; so did his "horseboxes", the long list of rectangles marked out on a piece of card before he went on any journey to a conference. Each "horsebox" would contain details of one advance job to be done; and each, when the job was finished, would be neatly ticked through. The routine never broke down; however numerous the changed appointments, the sudden demands, a confident voice would insist that there was no need to worry. "Always live a day at a time," he would add.

Outwardly, he took the strain remarkably well, although his doctor had advised caution only a few years after he had arrived in Scotland. In 1956 Appleton noted that he had "had to take notice of my doctors as regards outside activities," while four years later they were insisting that he "cut down outside activities to a minimum, and especially evening engagements, during term-time." The warning was not without its advantages. It could be used, and frequently was, as an excuse to evade outside activities and leave more time for the ionosphere.

To the constant burdens of overwork were increasingly added those created by his wife's health. To a very old friend he wrote, "She has been, psychologically, in great difficulties for years:" a condition troubling enough for any man in public life but doubly so for a Vice-Chancellor whose wife was naturally expected to accompany him, without erratic changes of mind, to a certain minimum of public functions. Still charming, still filling her role at Abden House, she had yet developed an unpredictability which was common knowledge to her husband's colleagues, and which could not be concealed from all his visitors.

Outside his own family he showed no visible reaction. Inside it, he admitted to the difference with London, where only he was concerned; here the University was also involved. But he had learned to be philosophic. He continued to "escape up into the ionosphere". The basic simplicity of his outlook and ambitions, which may somewhat have handicapped him in earlier years, now proved their worth. He could honestly say, "The older I grow the more I assess the importance of the simple uncomplicated qualities of loyalty and devotion to a cause or to an enterprise." For a decade he had two such enterprises, one the ionosphere, the other the University, and they were enough—or almost enough—to make him happy. He really did believe in Stevenson's claim that it is better to travel hopefully than to arrive. "As applied to life itself, Stevenson is surely right," he said. "Our happiness *does* come from the journey, from climbing and striving, from meeting the challenge of its difficulties. If you treat your professional job as a challenge to all your skill and attention, you'll have no need to look for at least one cause of happiness. You will perhaps realise some time afterwards that you've been intensely happy, even if you've been too busy to notice it at the time."

Appleton could say such things and convince even the most critical listeners of his sincerity. Just as he had a facility for enjoying the pomp without being pompous so could he at times describe life in Samuel

Smiles terms that yet appeared utterly convincing—an achievement for any man in the tough student world which had grown up round him during the post-war years.

He was fond of putting his beliefs, maxims, and aphorisms into his lectures and his letters. Many of them interestingly suggested lessons he had learned at Cambridge, or at the DSIR—"if you want something done, choose a busy man: the other kind has no time". "Many people," he noted, regarded "the study of philosophy as somewhat analagous to gnawing a bone, not much of a meal but extremely good for the teeth." As to scientific research and fishing, he thought they had much in common. "The only difference of which I am aware is this; that in scientific research you've got to tell the truth about what you catch." He tried, suggested a note in one of his little black books, "to think like a scientist—or academic, or professor, but not to talk like one". And while he was, he averred, a great believer in the ivory tower he believed, also, "in the stimulating value of coming down the stairs and out into the market place. For, very often, one encounters there the problems which one can take back into the ivory tower to ponder over, and perhaps even to solve." And he looked on students "not as vessels to be filled but as lamps to be lighted".

This attitude was underlined when, only a few years before his death, Appleton was asked which of his scientific awards had given him the greatest satisfaction. "I do not think that I would like to single out any award or scientific honour," he replied. "As a research supervisor I have had the great privilege of being associated with many young people starting out on their research careers. There has been something specially rewarding about seeing them succeed, grow in scientific stature, acquire responsibility in senior posts and, eventually, receive awards themselves. Yes, this is what has given me the greatest satisfaction."

It would be wrong to suggest that his interest in science—particularly in "Science for its own sake"—had been diminished by his experience in Edinburgh; but it had been to an extent qualified, with the larger theme of education in general taking over and enfolding the lesser theme of science. "Lesser", since Appleton was increasingly stressing the limitations of, as well as the prospects for, both science and scientists.

During the British Association meeting of 1953 he had warned his listeners during a popular lecture on "Science and the Public" that they must not "think that the authority of the scientist extends much beyond his own laboratory". Writing notes for a future lecture, he later said, "It is as wrong today to claim observation and experiment as the exclusive route to knowledge as it used to be to claim thinking alone as the only path to truth. At the least, the scientist should reflect, and reflect deeply, on the foundation of basic assumptions on which the edifice of experimental science has been erected."

These views were spelt out when he spoke on "Science and the Humanities" after receiving an honorary degree from Dalhousie University in 1958. "Some people speak of a rift and even an antagonism between science and the humanities, which seems odd to me because they deal with complementary aspects of human experience," he said. After pointing out that this adverse attitude towards science was by no means new, he returned "to the more serious charge that the modern scientist is a dangerous innovator, if not a downright barbarian. To my mind it is a charge that is based on a grave misconception of what science is, and of what the scientist professes to be. Above all we must recognise the limitations of science—limitations that the scientist is the first to acknowledge. Science does not pretend to supply us with what many men believe they have themselves derived from tradition and revelation. We cannot, by science—or, may I add, by logic, either—prove or disprove the existence of God. Science is only concerned with what can be observed by the senses and thus measured. It has nothing to say in the domain of morals, ethics or religion—the domain of what I would count even larger issues. And it behoves us to move with infinite caution when we seek to identify the connections between the disclosures of science and these larger issues—issues which confront us in the everyday world of thought and action, the world which asks, and has to decide, what is good or evil, what is right or wrong."

Although still deeply enmeshed in the day-to-day running of the University he was still being brought on to new government bodies such as the Lord President's new Radio Astronomy Planning Committee. He was still as eager as ever to discourse on the early days of the ionosphere, combining and recombining his reminiscences into "Some radio reflections", a title of which he was proud although he thought it was "not as good as Bernard Darwin's choice of 'Green Memories' for a book on golf".

Then, without warning, in the autumn of 1961, Lady Appleton suffered a severe stroke at Abden House. She was taken to one of the best nursing homes in Edinburgh, but it soon became clear that the chances of recovery were slim; it also appeared that the increasing difficulties of the three previous decades had probably been caused by brain-troubles which had begun in the late 1920's. One side of the brain had now gone; she was in no pain, but was partially paralysed and had no sense of time.

From now onwards, a new feature was added to the packed items of Appleton's diary. At least once a day he would visit the nursing home, squeezing in visits between conferences, meetings, and interviews, keeping his head above the stream largely through personal experience and the efforts of his assistants. At Abden House the pattern changed, with his daughter Margery, who with her husband had come to live in Edinburgh, acting as his hostess when necessary. He had already gained one pleasure from his daughter's move to Scotland, since it brought nearer her three children in whom he showed great interest during their earlier years. And when the eldest of them gained her degree at Edinburgh, Appleton showed particular pleasure.

From the start of 1962 Mrs. Allison added the background preparation of entertaining to her other duties, and for her Appleton had particular praise. "I am still working at the ionosphere in theoretical fashion even though I've no laboratory," he explained to Douglas Johnson, an old friend who had brought him much patent work before the war. "A lot of credit here should go to Mrs. Allison, for she makes it possible for me to find a little time for science, knowing that if I stopped doing research I should not be really happy. Actually I use *women mathematical students* to work at computations for me during the vacations. This brings them in money and is not too tiring. And, again, Mrs. Allison sees that they are fitted up with all they need." These students were Appleton's "IYL's" — Ionospheric Young Ladies — and for years a succession of them handled the routine mathematical work involved in processing the records sent to Edinburgh from all over the world.

He continued to "plug away". He continued to keep his own firm hand on the University, involving himself in far more work than many considered necessary. And with the George Square reconstruction by this time well under way he looked forward to the opening in the autumn of 1963 of the Hume Tower, the first of the new University blocks which were already rising on the east.

The Tower was to be opened on Monday, 21 October, by the Foreign Secretary, the Earl of Home. On Friday the 18th Appleton finished the speeches he was to make at the opening ceremony and at the dinner that evening, then confirmed that the special plaque to be unveiled was properly in position. That night it was announced that the Foreign Secretary had been appointed Prime Minister—"What Edinburgh University thinks today Her Majesty thinks tomorrow," commented Appleton—and it was soon afterwards clear that he would be unable to visit Edinburgh on the Monday. An urgent telephone call was made to Jo Grimond, the Liberal Leader, Rector of the University, then in his constituency of Orkney and Shetland. It was thought that he could accept and throughout Saturday, while Appleton rewrote his two speeches, the metal plaque was taken down and a hastily improvised glass affair put in its place. Late on Saturday, Grimond telephoned to regret that he, also, would be unable to come. On the Monday Appleton, having rewritten both speeches for the second time, himself unveiled yet another hastily prepared plaque.

He was by this time already becoming conscious of the retirement that lay 4 years away. Retirement from University administration, that is; as far as the ionosphere was concerned much remained to be done, and he had no plans for moving from Edinburgh. But he did want some house to which he could go for the week-ends, for holidays and, after he had retired, for three or four months in the summer. He would need somewhere within reasonable distance and had for some time been visiting the attractive rolling peninsula of Fife, gripped between the Firths of Forth and Tay and soon to be brought nearer to the capital by the new Forth road bridge. And late in 1964 he bought a house in the small Fife village of Elie that admirably suited his requirements. Facing the Forth, only an hour from the centre of Edinburgh, to which he could easily commute, it provided an ideal home for the years ahead.

It was clear that retirement would not mean rustication, and in the autumn of 1964 this was underlined when moves were put in hand to forward Appleton's name for a life peerage. He would, indeed, have made an admirable member of the Upper House, experienced as he was in the peculiar problems of the area where science and administration meet. He would have loved the pageantry, spoken well, and no doubt proved an ornament as well as a useful work-horse for the Conservative peers—provided always, of course, that he could have found time for yet additional duties south of the Border. However, whatever chances there were of Appleton's reaching the Lords were douched, if not des-troyed, by the Socialists' victory of October 1964.

A few weeks later Lady Appleton died, and for her funeral Appleton returned, once again, to his native Bradford. He had not taken a great interest in the City since being made a Freeman 16 years previously, a point noted by some of the City officials and one not totally explicable in terms of his heavy load of work.

Back in Edinburgh he began to reorganise his life once again. There was a full schedule of University work ahead for the New Year, a good many ionospheric problems which he had discussed in detail with Piggott, and a number of international conferences. He had, moreover, been invited to visit Norway where at Geilo he was to speak to radio physicists on the early days of ionospheric investigations.

In the New Year he announced his engagement to Mrs. Allison, his Private Secretary, to the pleasure of their mutual friends both inside and outside the University, most of whom knew how for 13 years she had helped to organise his official life to keep time free for scientific work.

In February he opened the new Napier Technical College in Edin-burgh—showing his usual facility for digging down into the Scottish background—and on 17 March, the University's new wind tunnel, one of the necessarily expensive projects he had helped push through official channels during the previous few years. The latter was the first official appointment since his engagement, and while he made the speech for the occasion he insisted that Mrs. Allison start the tunnel's machinery. "She pushed the button and I made the speech", as he afterwards put it.

A few days later he was quietly married in Canongate Kirk by his friend, Dr. Selby Wright. It was a purely family occasion followed by a lunch party at Abden House. After a short honeymoon at Torquay he returned with his wife to Edinburgh for a few days to see his mother-in-law to whom he was deeply attached. Then they went to Elie for a further 10 days' holiday.

The new term had not yet started and he had time to make plans for the future, particularly for the ionospheric work he had already discussed with Beynon and Piggott. He must have been happier than at almost any other time in his life, looking forward to great things ahead.

Appleton returned to Edinburgh in time for the start of term, took the Chair at the University Court and was in his office the following two days in his usual good form. On the Wednesday night, exactly a month after his marriage, he died in Abden House, without premonition, only minutes after discussing plans for the future, the victim of sudden heart failure.

Those who were close to Sir Edward knew that he had been an extremely happy man during the weeks leading up to his sudden death, for to the joy of his second marriage there was added the satisfaction of resolving an ionospheric anomaly that had intrigued him for many years. His early publications had drawn attention to unexpected seasonal variations in the E-layer ionization density at different latitudes, and it is possible to see a constant question about these variations running through the papers written at Edinburgh—87 of them in all. "It seemed", says Professor Farvis of Edinburgh University's School of Engineering Science, "that he had been methodically clearing away over the years some of the smaller influences and effects one by one, in order that some major factor might be recognised. In those last few weeks, after several months work, the answers to the questions he had been framing on latitude effects seemed to reveal something to him about E-layer behaviour which really excited him".

It seemed that he was surprised and delighted by the answers his results were producing; but the paper in which he was describing these was unfinished at the time of his death. However, enough clues were found among his papers for others to take up the lead he had found. Dr. Muggleton, a Senior Lecturer in the University of Edinburgh, has fitted most of the pieces into the jig-saw puzzle, and is successfully continuing the research after publishing an edited version of Sir Edward's unfinished MS article.

All this lay in the future as on the morning of 21 April Edinburgh's flags were unexpectedly lowered to half-mast, a tribute to someone who had successfully pulled the City's University through one of its most difficult patches. There were to be others, during the months that followed, from a wider field. The impressive Memorial Service in St. Giles Cathedral was followed by the creation of more than one Lecture in Appleton's memory—those founded by URSI in collaboration with the Royal Society, by the Institution of Electrical Engineers, and by the Edinburgh University Physical Society, a student body.

Almost two years later the University's Appleton Tower was opened, a massive block initially known as the First Year Science Building, but renamed on the suggestion of the new Principal, Professor Michael Swann. When it was opened by Lady Appleton she unveiled, at the same time, a showcase in the building containing all Sir Edward's orders and decorations and the Freedom of the City of Bradford Casket.

All this was no more than was proper for a man who had successfully climbed the long scientific ladder and established a place for himself at the top. Just as fitting was the decision of the International Astronomical Union's Executive Committee to accept the recommendation of its Commission of the Moon in 1970 that Appleton should be one of the scientists after whom a feature on the moon should be named. Yet Appleton's achievement had been something slightly more and something slightly different from this. From that day in the middle twenties when he had first shown the existence of the ionosphere he had determined to remain, as long as possible, the leading master in the new science of ionospheric investigation whose creation he had foreseen. Thus the levers of power—except where they concerned the world of the ionosphere—had failed to interest him greatly; even in the field of radar, for whose evolution his work had provided an important tool, he did not wish to get involved in "the circus of political self-seekers". By contrast, he was always rightly anxious to be recognised for his own sake, for what he had achieved in his own particular world, the outcome of an inner mixture of surprise and pride when he looked back to his Bradford boyhood, an experience from which he was never able entirely to escape.

This complex of scientific dedication and almost Victorian pride in success, at times complicated by the tribulations of a none-too-happy home life, would have been unbearable for a man of less equable and less rugged character than Appleton. His ability to keep his head amid the turmoil had made him, in the field of public affairs, an admirable choice for the secretaryship of the DSIR during the difficult days of the war; in much the same way, his level-headed personal discernment of the things that really mattered had helped to damp down conflicting feelings that might have torn apart different men. His epitaph might well be provided by an earlier President of the British Association, T. H. Huxley, writing to a friend after he had at last found his feet: "I have had a hard fight of it but as things go I must count myself singularly fortunate. The man should be thankful who has found his work and has only got to do it."

BIBLIOGRAPHY

1918

A thermionic valve slopemeter, *Wireless World*, 6 November.

Note on the production of continuous electrical oscillations by the three-electrode valve, *Electrician*, December.

1919

Note on the effects of grid currents in three-electrode ionic tubes, *Phil. Mag.* 37, 129.

1921

A method of testing triode vacuum tubes, *Proc. Camb. Phil. Soc.* 20, 239.

A method of demonstrating the retroactive property of a triode oscillator, *Proc. Phys. Soc. Lond.* 33, 100.

On the function of the variable anode tap connection in triode generators, *Radio Rev.* 2 August.

(With Balth van der Pol, Jr.), On the form of free triode vibrations, *Phil. Mag.* 42, 201.

1922

(With Balth van der Pol, Jr.), On a type of oscillation-hysteresis in a simple triode generator, *Phil. Mag.* 43, 177.

(With A. D. Robb), On a graphical solution of a class of differential equations occurring in wireless telegraphy, *Phil. Mag.* 43, 214.

The automatic synchronization of triode oscillators, *Proc. Camb. Phil. Soc.* 21, 231.

1923

(With W. M. H. Greaves), On the solution of the representative differential equation of the triode oscillator, *Phil. Mag.* 45, 401.

(With R. A. Watson-Watt), On the nature of atmospherics: I, *Proc. Roy. Soc.* A, 103, 84.

(With A. G. D. West), On ionic oscillations in the striated glow discharge, *Phil. Mag.* 45, 879.

(With Mary Taylor), On optimum heterodyne reception (note: by the editor of an unidentified journal, 10 November 1923, and reprinted on pp. 277–93.)

221

Sir Edward Appleton

1924

(With F. S. Thompson) Periodic trigger reception. *J. Inst. Elec. Engrs.* **62**, 181.

(With K. G. Emeleus and M. A. F. Barnett), Some experiments with an alpha-particle counter, *Proc. Camb. Phil. Soc.* **22**, 434.

On the anomalous behaviour of a vibration galvanometer, *Phil. Mag.* **47**, 609.

1925

A discussion on geophysical influences on the transmission of wireless waves, *Proc. Phys. Soc. Lond.* **37**, 16D.

(With M. A. F. Barnett), Local reflection of wireless waves from the upper atmosphere, *Nature, Lond.* **115**, 333.

Discussion by E. V. Appleton on the paper Comparison of frequencies by cathode-ray tube by D. W. Dye, *Proc. Phys. Soc.* **37**, April 1925, 158–66, 166–8.

(With M. A. F. Barnett), Wireless wave propagation, the magnetic-ionic theory: the part played by the atmosphere; the effect of diurnal variations, *Electrician* **94**, 398.

(With M. A. F. Barnett), On some direct evidence for downward atmospheric reflection of electric rays, *Proc. Roy. Soc.* A, **109**, 621.

(With M. A. F. Barnett), A note on wireless signal strength measurements made during the solar eclipse of 24 January 1925, *Proc. Camb. Phil. Soc.* **22**, 674.

Geophysical influences on the transmission of wireless waves, *Proc. Phys. Soc. Lond.* **37**, 16D.

Problemen Bij de Uitbreiding van Electro-magnetische Golven. Overdruk uit het, *Tijdschr. Nederlandsch Radiogenootschap*, November.

1926

(With R. A. Watson-Watt and J. F. Herd), On the nature of atmospherics: Parts II and III, *Proc. Roy. Soc.* A, **111**, 615, 654.

Contribution to Discussion on the electrical state of the upper atmosphere, *Proc. Roy. Soc.* III, 1 May 1926.

The Kerr effect in wireless transmission, *Nature, Lond.* **118**, 514.

(With M. A. F. Barnett), On wireless interference phenomenon between ground waves and waves deviated by the upper atmosphere, *Proc. Roy. Soc.* A, **113**, 450.

On the diurnal variation of ultra-short wave wireless transmission, *Proc. Camb. Phil. Soc.* **23**, 155.

1927

Magnetic storms and wireless transmission, *Electronics* **98**, 256.

(With J. A. Ratcliffe), On the nature of wireless signal variations, *Proc. Roy. Soc.* A, **115**, 291.

The existence of more than one ionized layer in the upper atmosphere, *Nature, Lond.* **120**, 330.

Magnetic storms and wireless transmission, *Electrician*, March.

The influence of the earth's magnetic field on wireless transmission, URSI. Papers of the General Assembly, Washington, Fasc. 1, 2.

Wireless transmission and the upper atmosphere, Royal Institution of Great Britain, Weekly Evening Meeting, April, *Proc. R. Instn. Gt. Br.* **25**, 272.

The existence of more than one ionized layer in the upper atmosphere, reprinted from Part 1, Vol. 1, 128, papers of the General Assembly of URSI, held Washington, October.

Bibliography

1928

The study of signal fading, *J. Instn. Elect. Engrs.* **66**, 872.

(With J. A. Ratcliffe), On a method of determining the state of polarization of down-coming wireless waves, *Proc. Roy. Soc.* A, **117**, 576.

Some notes on wireless methods of investigating the electrical structure of the upper atmosphere, *Proc. Phys. Soc. Lond.* **41**, 43.

1929

Some large-scale optical experiments, *The School Science Review*, No. 39, March.

The equivalent heights of the atmospheric ionized regions in England and America, *Nature, Lond.* **123**, 445.

1930

On some measurements of the equivalent height of the atmospheric ionized layer, *Proc. Roy. Soc.* A, **126**, 542.

Some notes on wireless methods of investigating the electrical structure of the upper atmosphere: II, *Proc. Phys. Soc. Lond.* **42**, 321.

(With J. A. Ratcliffe), Some simultaneous observations on downcoming wireless waves, *Proc. Roy. Soc.* A, **128**, 133.

(With A. L. Green), On some short wave equivalent height measurements of the ionized regions of the upper atmosphere, *Proc. Roy. Soc.* A, **128**, 159.

(With E. C. Childs), On some radio frequency properties of ionized air, *Phil. Mag.* **10**, 969.

1931

A method of measuring upper atmosphere ionization, *Nature, Lond.* **127**, 197.

(With G. Builder), A simple method of investigating wireless echoes of short delay, *Nature, Lond.* **127**, 970.

Polarization of downcoming wireless waves in the southern hemisphere, *Nature, Lond.* **128**, 1037.

1932

(With G. Builder), Wireless echoes of short delay, *Proc. Phys. Soc. Lond.* **44**, 76.

(With F. W. Chapman), The collisional friction experienced by vibrating electrons in ionized air, *Proc. Phys. Soc. Lond.* **44**, 246.

(With D. Boohariwalla), The mutual interference of wireless signals in simultaneous detection, *Wireless Engineer and Experimental Wireless*, March.

(With W. H. Aldous), *Thermionic Vacuum Tubes*, Methuen.

(With S. Chapman), Suggested wireless observations during the solar eclipse of 31 August 1932, *Nature, Lond.* **129**, 757.

(With R. Naismith), Some measurements of upper atmosphere ionization, *Proc. Roy. Soc.* A, **137**, 36.

(With D. W. Fray), Wireless signals: Their mutual influence in simultaneous detection, *Electrician*, 15 July.

(With J. A. Ratcliffe), Polarization of wireless echoes, *Nature, Lond.* **130**, 472.

Wireless studies of the ionosphere, *Proc. Instn. Elect. Engrs.* **71**, 642.

1933

(With G. Builder), The ionosphere as a doubly refracting medium, *Proc. Phys. Soc. Lond.* **45**, 208.

223

Sir Edward Appleton

(With R. Naismith), Weekly measurements of upper atmospheric ionization, *Proc. Phys. Lond.* **45**, 389.
Fine-structure of the ionosphere, *Nature, Lond.* **131**, 872.
(With R. Naismith and G. Builder), Ionospheric investigations in high latitudes, *Nature, Lond.* **132**, 340.
On two methods of ionospheric investigation, *Proc. Phys. Soc. Lond.* **45**, 673.
(With others), Meeting for discussion of the ionosphere, *Proc. Roy. Soc.* A, **141**, 697.
(With E. G. Bowen), Sources of atmospherics and penetrating radiation, *Nature, Lond.* **132**, 965.
Radio observations during the International Polar Year 1932–3, Royal Institution of Great Britain, Weekly Evening Meeting, October, *Proc. R. Instn. Gt. Br.* **28**, 1.
Empire communication: the Norman Lockyer Lecture, 1933, the British Science Guild, November.

1934
Radio exploration of the ionosphere, *Nature, Lond.* **133**, 793.
(With F. W. Chapman), The lightning flash as source of an atmospheric, *Nature, Lond.* **134**, 968.

1935
Recent measurements of upper-atmospheric ionization, *Phys. Rev.* **47**, 89.
A method of measuring the collisional frequency of electrons in the ionosphere, *Nature, Lond.* **135**, 618.
(With S. Chapman), Report on ionization changes during a solar eclipse, *Proc. Inst. Radio Engrs.* **23**, 658.
Temperature changes in the higher atmosphere, *Nature, Lond.* **136**, 52.
(With R. Naismith), Some further measurements of upper atmospheric ionization, *Proc. Roy. Soc.* A, **150**, 685.
(With L. J. Ingram), Magnetic storms and upper atmospheric ionization, *Nature, Lond.* **136**, 548.
(With D. B. Boohariwalla), The influence of a magnetic field on the high frequency conductivity of an ionized medium, *Proc. Phys. Soc. Lond.* **47**, 1074.
The seasonal variation of ionization in Region F_2 of the ionosphere, *Phys. Rev.* **47**, 704.
(With D. B. Boohariwalla), The influence of a magnetic field on the high-frequency conductivity of an ionized medium, *Proc. Phys. Soc. Lond.* **47**, 1074.
Temperature changes in the higher atmosphere, *Nature, Lond.* **136**, 52.

1936
Some problems of atmospheric physics, 1st Cobb Lecture, Royal Society of Arts, 16 November 1936 (never printed).
Interruptions in shortwave communication, *World Radio* **23**, 9.

1937
(With F. W. Chapman), On the nature of atmospherics: IV, *Proc. Roy. Soc.* A, **158**, 1.
(With R. Naismith and L. J. Ingram), British radio observations during the Second International Polar Year 1932–3, *Phil. Trans.* A, **236**, 191.
Regularities and irregularities in the ionosphere, *Proc. Roy. Soc.* A, **162**, 451.

Bibliography

1938

(With J. H. Piddington), The reflexion coefficients of ionosphere regions, *Proc. Roy. Soc. A*, **164**, 467.

(With F. T. Farmer and J. A. Ratcliffe), Magnetic double refraction of medium radio waves in the ionosphere, *Nature, Lond.* **141**, 409.

(With K. Weekes), Tides in the upper atmosphere, *Nature, Lond.* **142**, 71.

Radio transmission and solar activity, *Nature, Lond.* **142**, 499.

Note on a method of investigating the interaction of radio waves, *Int. Sci. Radio Un., Proc. Gen. Assembly, 1938*, **5**, 23.

(With K. Weekes), Tides in the upper atmosphere., *Int. Sci. Radio Un., Proc. Gen. Assembly, 1938*, **5**, 71.

(With J. Sayers), Recombination in the ionosphere. *Int. Sci. Radio Un., Proc. Gen. Assembly, 1938*, **5**, 272.

(With R. Naismith), Report of Ionospheric Subcommission of Commission: II, *Int. Sci. Radio Un., Proc. Gen. Assembly, 1938*, **5**, 313.

Remarks on Dr. Chapman's note on radio fade-outs and the associated magnetic disturbances, *J. Geophys. Res.* **43**, 487.

1939

The ionosphere, *Occ. Notes Res. Astr. Soc.* **3**, 33.

(With R. Naismith and L. J. Ingram), The critical frequency method of measuring upper atmospheric ionization, *Proc. Phys. Soc. Lond.* **51**, 81.

(With R. Naismith), Scattering of radio waves in the polar regions, *Nature, Lond.* **143**, 243.

(With R. Naismith), The variation of solar ultraviolet radiation during the sunspot cycle, *Phil. Mag.* **27**, 144.

(With K. Weekes), On lunar tides in the upper atmosphere, *Proc. Roy. Soc. A*, **171**, 171.

Characteristic variation of Region F_2 ionization throughout the year, *Nature, Lond.* **144**, 151.

The upper atmosphere—the structure of the atmosphere as deduced from ionospheric observations, *Quart. J. Roy. Met. Soc.* **65**, 324.

New Materials for Old, 46th James Forrest Lecture, *J. Instn. Civil Engnrs.* Session 1939–40.

1940

(With R. Naismith), Normal and abnormal region-E ionization, *Proc. Phys. Soc. Lond.* **52**, 402.

(With W. J. G. Beynon), The application of ionospheric data to radio communication problems: Pt. I, *Proc. Soc. Lond.* **52**, 518.

1942

Plastics and their application, *Endeavour* **1**(3), July.

Ionospheric Influence of Geomagnetism (The Guthrie Lecture), unpublished.

1943

A simple method of demonstrating the circular polarization of ionospherically reflected radio waves, *Nature, Lond.* **141**, 250.

Note on the Morphology of the F_2 Layer of the Ionosphere, DSIR, No. 39 (Secret).

1944

Second note on the Morphology of the F₂ Layer of the Ionosphere, DSIR, No. 42, 8
August (Confidential).

1945

The Scientist in wartime, 32nd Thomas Hawksley Lecture, *Proc. I. Mech. E.* **154.**
The scientific princples of radio location, 36th Kelvin Lecture, *J. Instn. Elect. Engrs.*
92, 340.
Departure of long-wave solar radiation from black-body intensity, *Nature, Lond.* **156,**
534.

1946

(With J. S. Hey), Solar radio noise: I, *Phil. Mag.* **37,** 73.
Extra-tropospheric influences on ultra-short-wave radar operation, *J. Instn. Elect. Engrs.*
93, 110.
Two anomalies in the ionosphere, *Nature, Lond.* **157,** 691.
(With J. S. Hey), Circular polarization of radio noise, *Nature, Lond.* **158,** 339.
(With R. Naismith), Radar detection of meteor trails, *Nature, Lond.* **158,** 936.
Radar development and scientific radio research, Halley Lecture, Oxford (not
published).
Terrestrial magnetism and the ionosphere, Rede Lecture, Cambridge (not published).

1947

(With W. J. G. Beynon), The application of ionospheric data to radio communication
problems: Pt. II, *Proc. Phys. Soc. Lond.* **59,** 58.
(With R. Naismith), The radio detection of meteor trails and allied phenomena, *Proc.
Phys. Soc. Lond.* **59,** 461.
Geomagnetic control of F₂-layer ionization, *Science* **106,** 17.
The investigation and forecasting of ionospheric conditions, *J. Instn. Elect. Engrs.* **94,**
186.
The Influence of Tropospheric Conditions on Ultra-short-wave Propagation, Physical and
Royal Meteorological Societies' Report, p. 1.
Earth, stars, and radio, Address to Section A, Mathematics and Physics, British Asso-
ciation, *Nature, Lond.* **160,** 1283.
The practical importance of fundamental research, 30th Earl Grey Memorial Lecture.

1948

(With W. J. G. Beynon and W. R. Piggott), Anomalous effects in ionospheric absorp-
tion, *Nature, Lond.* **161,** 967.
The electron in theory and practice, 2nd Dunn Memorial Lecture, *Chem. and Ind.*, pp.
819–26.
(With W. R. Piggott), *Ionospheric Absorption Measurements Throughout a Sunspot
Cycle*, The British National Committee for Scientific Radio.
(With W. J. G. Beynon), Lunar tidal oscillations in the ionosphere, *Nature, Lond.* **162,**
486.

1949

The organization and work of the Department of Scientific and Industrial Research,
39th May. Lecture to the Institute of Metals, 25th May 1949, *J. Inst. Metals* **75** (12).

Bibliography

(With W. J. G. Beynon), Lunar oscillations in the D-layer of the ionosphere, *Nature, Lond.* **164**, 308.
Discussion on the investigation and forecasting of ionospheric conditions, *Proc. Instn. Elect. Engrs.* **96** (III), 213.

1950
(With W. R. Piggott), World morphology of ionospheric storms, *Nature, Lond.* **165**, 130.
Radio waves of extra-terrestrial origin, Presidential address to the Science Masters Assoc., 3rd Jan. 1949, *School Science Review*, No. 114.
Magnetic and ionospheric storms, *Arch. Met. (Wien)* **3**, 113.
Magnetic and ionospheric storms, *Archiv. für Meteorologie, Geophysik und Bioklimatologie, Serie A*; *Meteorologie und Geophysik*, Band III, 1–2 Heft.
Oliver Heaviside, 1850–1925, *Discovery*, July 1950.
Studies of the F_2-layer in the ionosphere: I, The position of the ionospheric equator in the F_2-layer, *J. Atmos. Terr. Phys.* **1**, 106.

1952
(With W. R. Piggott), The morphology of storms in the F_2-layer of the ionosphere: I, Some statistical relationships, *J. Atmos. Terr. Phys.* **2**, 236.
Opening of IRE radio engineering convention in Australia, IRE (Aust.) Radio Engineering Supplement, *Radio Electrical Weekly*, 5 September.

1953
Storm phenomena in the ionosphere, *Arch. Elektr. Ubertr.* **7**, 271.
(With W. J. G. Beynon), Radio communication on frequencies exceeding predicted values, *Proc. Instn. Elect. Engrs.* **100**, 192.
(With W. R. Piggott), Ionospheric storms and the geomagnetic anomaly in the F_2-layer, *J. Atmos. Terr. Phys.* **3**, 121.
A note on the "sluggishness" of the ionosphere, *J. Atmos. Terr. Phys.* **3**, 282.
Geomagnetism and the ionosphere, Scientific Papers, *Tribute to Max Born*, pp. 1–11.

1954
(With W. R. Piggott), Storm phenomena and the solar cycle variations of the F_2-layer ionization at noon, *Physics of the Ionosphere*, p. 219, London, The Physical Society.
(With A. J. Lyon), Ionospheric layer formation under quasi-stationary conditions, *Physics of the Ionosphere*, p. 20. London, the Physical Society.
(With W. R. Piggott), Ionosphere absorption measurements during a sunspot cycle, *J. Atmos. Terr. Phys.* **5**, 141.
The anomalous equatorial belt in the F_2-layer, *J. Atmos. Terr. Phys.* **5**, 348.

1955
Opening Address at Symposium on the Upper Atmosphere, 16 July 1954, *Quart. J. Royal Met. Soc.* **81** (347), January.
(With W. J. G. Beynon), An ionospheric attenuation equivalence theorem, *J. Atmos. Terr. Phys.* **6**, 141.
(With A. J. Lyon and Mrs. A. G. Pritchard), The detection of the Sq current system in ionospheric radio sounding, *J. Atmos. Terr. Phys.* **7**, 292.

Sir Edward Appleton

(With A. J. Lyon and Mrs. A. G. Turnbull), Distortion of the E-layer of the ionosphere by electrical currents flowing in it, *Nature, Lond.* **176**, 897.

Rocket sounding in the upper air, confirmation of results inferred from radio measurements by E. V. Appleton, reprinted from *Wireless World*, September, Y10–Y11, pp. 406–7.

1956

Regularities and irregularities in the ionosphere, reprinted from *Vistas in Astronomy* (ed. A. Beer), Vol. 2, Pergamon Press, London and New York.

1957

(With A. J. Lyon), Studies of the E-layer of the ionosphere: I, Some relevant theoretical relationships, *J. Atmos. Terr. Phys.* **10**, 1.

1959

The normal E region of the ionosphere, *Proc. Inst. Radio Engrs.* **47**, 155.

Equatorial anomalies in the F_2-layer of the ionosphere, *Proceedings of the 1959 September URSI Meeting held in Brussels.*

Global morphology of the E- and F_1-layers of the ionosphere, *J. Atmos. Terr. Phys.* **15**, 9.

1960

Tides in the Atmosphere, 1st Kelvin Lecture, abbreviate to *Proc. Roy. Phil. Soc. Glasgow*, delivered 3rd February.

1961

(With A. J. Lyon), Studies of the E-layer of the ionosphere: II, Electromagnetic perturbations and other anomalies, *J. Atmos. Terr. Phys.* **21**, 73.

Sir Joseph Larmor and the ionosphere, *Proc. Roy. Irish Acad.* **61**, 55.

1962

Radio and the ionosphere, *Nature, Lond.* **195**, 225.

1963

Ionospheric consequences of the earth's orbital eccentricity, *Nature, Lond.* **197**, 1239.

A seasonal anomaly in the ionospheric E-layer, *J. Atmos. Terr. Phys.* **25**, 577.

Moderne Ionosphärenforschung, *Naturwissenschaftliche Rundschau* Sonderdruck aus, Band 16, Heft 10, Oktober, Seite 381–8.

A seasonal anomaly in the ionospheric E-layer, *J. Atmos. Terr. Phys.* **25**, 577–9.

1964

Sunspot-cycle control of ionospheric and geomagnetic variations, *J. Atmos. Terr. Phys.* **26**, 633–40.

The science of near space, 10th Graham Clark Lecture, *Electronics and Power*, May, pp. 140–5.

1965

The E-layer of the ionosphere, for the *International Dictionary of Geophysics* (this article was being prepared by E. V. Appleton at the time of his death in April 1965 and it has been completed and edited by W. J. G. Beynon).

OTHER SELECTED WRITINGS

1937

Marconi, *The Listener*, 20 July.

1945

Sequence of discoveries, *The Listener*, 16 August.
How radiolocation works, *The Listener*, 23 August.

1947

The Ionosphere, Nobel Prize Lecture.

1949

Commentary: The scientist in industry, *Research*, 2.

1950

Cosmic exploration by radio, *The Times*.

1953

Science for its own sake, Presidential Address to the British Association for the Advancement of Science, No. 38, 103.
Finding things out with radio and rockets, Junior Presidential Address to the British Association, September.

1954

Report of the Scottish Peat Committee.

1955

Storms in the ionosphere, *Endeavour*, **14**, 24.
The Advantages of VHF, *The Listener*, 26 May, pp. 925–6.
Experiments in concert—The International Geophysical Year of 1957–1958, *The Times*, January.
Supply of Teachers of Mathematics and Science in Scotland, Report of the Appleton Committee, March.
Science and invention in communications and electronics, reprinted in *British Communications and Electronics*, **2** (11), November.

Sir Edward Appleton

1957

The pattern of scientific research in Britain, Address at Fiftieth Anniversary of the Graduate School of Arts and Sciences, Cincinnati, 8 March.

Medicine: a science and a humanity, reprinted from *Journal of the Royal College of Surgeons of Edinburgh*, **2**, 251–5, June.

1958

Science and the humanities, Address at Special Convocation of Dalhousie University, 10 September.

1959

University in development, *The Scotsman*, 21 April.

Radar detection of nuclear tests—geophysical effects at high altitude, *Glasgow Herald*, 20 August.

Science and communication, 1st British Association Granada Lecture, 13 October.

1961

The origins of radio noise: The radio noise spectrum by Donald H. Menzel, *New Scientist*, No. 222, 16 February.

The Young Rutherford, in *The Collected Papers of Lord Rutherford*, George Allen and Unwin.

1965

Shortage of science applicants to universities, *Nature, Lond.* **205**, 232–3, 16 January.

HONOURS AND DECORATIONS

Nobel Prizeman and Medallist.
Fellow of The Royal Society.
Foreign Member, American Academy of Arts and Sciences.
Foreign Member, Royal Norwegian Academy of Sciences.
Foreign Member, Royal Swedish Academy of Science.
Honorary Member, Australian Institution of Radio Engineers.
Honorary Member, Royal Belgian Society of Engineers and Industrialists.
Honorary Member, Institution of Civil Engineers.
Honorary Member, Institution of Mechanical Engineers.
Honorary Member, Institution of Electrical Engineers.
Honorary Member, Royal Irish Academy (in Section of Science).
Honorary Member, Royal Institution of British Architects.
Honorary Member, American Meteorological Society.
Honorary Member, American Academy of Arts and Sciences.
Member, Pontifical Academy of Sciences.
Honorary Fellow, National Institute of Sciences of India.
Honorary Fellow, the Royal Institute of Chemistry.
Corresponding Member, Prussian Academy of Science.
Foreign Member, Deutsche Akademie der Wissenschaften zu Berlin.
Corresponding Member, Mainz Academy of Science and Letters.
Honorary Fellow, St John's College, Cambridge.
Honorary Freeman of Bradford, Yorkshire.
Honorary Fellow, Royal College of Surgeons of Edinburgh.
Honorary Member of Cincinnati Medical Academy.
Honorary Fellow, Royal Society of Edinburgh.
Fellow, King's College, London.
Honorary Member, U.K. and Eire Section of the I.E.E.E.

231

Sir Edward Appleton

HONORARY DEGREES

Hon. LL.D. Aberdeen, Birmingham, St Andrews, London, Glasgow, Liverpool, and Dalhousie.
Hon. D.Sc. Oxford, Brussels, Leeds, Sydney, Sheffield and Laval.
Hon. Sc.D. Cambridge.
Hon. Litt.D. Cincinnati.
Hon. D.Eng. Hannover Technische Hochschule.
Hon. Doc. Montreal.

DECORATIONS

G.B.E., K.C.B., Medal of Merit (U.S.A.); Legion of Honour (France); Cross of Freedom (Norway); Commander with Star, Order of Saint Olav (Class II); Knight Commander with Star of the Icelandic Order of the Falcon.

MEDALS

M.A., D.Sc.	DEGREES
Royal	Royal Society.
Hughes	Royal Society.
Alfred Ewing	Civil Engineers.
Faraday	Institution of Electrical Engineers.
Chree	Physical Society.
Albert	Royal Society of Arts.
Poulsen	Danish Academy of Technical Science.
Transeater	Belgium.
Indian	Calcutta University (the Sir Debaprasad Sarbadhikary Gold Medal).
Medal of Honour	Norwegian Polytechnical Society.
Medal of Honour	Institute of Radio Engineers of America.
Kelvin	Joint Engineering Institutions' award.
Keith	Royal Scottish Society of Arts.

INDEX

Abden House 161, 162–4, 174, 214, 217
Adelaide, Australia 199
Admiralty's Scientific Research Service 30, 106, 121
Admiralty Signals Experimental Establishment 99, 136
Advisory Committee on Medical Research 172–3
Agricultural Research Council 162
Aircraft Production, Ministry of 125
Air Ministry 30, 123, 134, 181
Akers, Sir Wallace 121, 125–6, 127, 128
Albert's Workshop, Prince 58
Alder, L. S. B. 98–99
Alder–Salmond patent 99, 138
Aldershot 13, 14, 29, 158
Aldous, W. H. 27
Alexandrian Quartette 3
Allison, Mrs. Helen 174, 197, 198, 214, 216–17
Alness, 1st Baron 162
Anderson, Sir John 124, 125, 128, 142
Andrade, Professor E. N. da Costa 186, 209
Anglo-Swedish Society 171
Appleton, Dorothy (sister) 8
Appleton, Edward Victor
  birth 3
  early years in Bradford 3–8
  at Cambridge, 1911–14 8–12
  marries 15

  during First World War 12–18
  at Cambridge 1920 20–48
  measures height of ionosphere 36–48
  at King's College, London 49–92
  in northern Norway 76–87
  at the Halley Stewart Laboratory 88–92
  Cambridge, 1936–8 93–106
  joins Tizard Committee 102–3
  secretary of D.S.I.R. 106–41
  Nobel Prize for Physics 145–7
  Principal and Vice-Chancellor, Edinburgh University 160–218
  death of wife 216
  remarries 217
  death 217
  feature on moon named after 218
Appleton, Lady Helen (wife) 217
Appleton, Isabel (sister) 4, 7–8
Appleton, James (grandfather) 3
Appleton, Lady Jessie (wife) 15, 26, 49, 50, 114, 116, 158–9, 199
  health of 73–74, 88, 211, 214, 216
Appleton, Margery (daughter) 26, 50, 73, 89, 114, 214
Appleton, Mary (mother) 3
Appleton, Peter (father) 3, 4, 88, 145
Appleton, Rosalind (daughter) 50, 89, 114, 116, 147, 199
Appleton Hut 95
"Appleton's Journal" 196

233

Index

Index

Index

Index

Index

Index

Index

Television 68–69, 91, 113, 148–9
Thermionic Vacuum Tubes 27
Thermionic valves 18, 24
"Thermionic valve slopemeter" 19
Thompson, Silvanus 6
Thomson, Sir G. P. 21, 123, 124
Thomson, Sir J. J. ix, 6, 8–9, 10, 20, 167
Three Steps to Victory x
Times, The 69, 175, 189
Tirpitz 140
Tizard, Sir Henry x, 97, 102, 103–5, 106, 119, 120, 121, 124, 133, 135–8, 159, 168, 204, 207
Tizard Committee 100, 102, 121–2, 123, 157
Torquay 217
Townsend, Professor 31
Townsend Electrical Laboratory, Oxford 41, 43
Trippe, Captain 14, 31
Trollope, Anthony 174
Tromso, Norway 77, 78, 79–86, 140
Tube Alloys 120–1, 123, 124–8
Turnbull, Mrs. (later Pritchard) 173, 193, 194
Tuve x, 45, 62

Ultra Short Wave Panel 133–4, 154
United Nations High Commission for Refugees 201
United States Information Services 192
University Court 168, 173–4
University Grants Committee 150, 171, 184, 202
University Industrial Liaison Committee 159
URSI (International Scientific Radio Union) 59, 75–76, 131, 143–4, 193, 198–9, 217
URSI General Assemblies 198–9
Usher Hall, Edinburgh 203

Van der Pol, Balthazar 24–27, 76, 140
correspondence with 26, 28–29, 31, 40, 43, 44, 49–50, 69–70, 195
Verity, J. A. 6, 7
V2 rockets 152

Wallace, Alfred Russell 38
Wallis, Barnes 111
War Memorial Lecture, Sydney 199
War Office 192
Washington 127–8
Water Pollution Research Laboratory 111
Watson-Watt, Sir Robert x, 29, 51, 53, 56, 63, 76, 78, 86, 87, 96–98, 101–2, 102–3, 104, 107, 121, 132, 135–8, 155–8
Weekes, Kenneth 94–95
West, Captain 42
West Riding Regiment 12
Whiddington, Robert 143
Wilkins, A. F. x, 101, 157
William IV 116
Wilson, C. T. R. 21, 26, 28, 33, 64, 93, 184
Wiltshire Prize 7, 10
Wimperis, H. E. x, 100–1, 101–2, 103–4
Windsor Castle 126
Wireless World 19
Woolton, Frederick James, 1st Baron 117
Wright, Dr. Selby 217

York, Duke and Duchess of 71
Yorkshire Post 7
Young, Geoffrey Winthrop 209

Zeesen 151–2
Zuckerman, Sir Solly 159
Zurich 198